bild

Personal Development and Reflective Practice in a Learning Disability Service

Alice Bradley

Supporting the Learning Disability Awards Framework

Higher Professional Diploma in Learning Disability Services (Level 4)

Unit 3: Personal Development and Reflective Practice in a Learning Disability Service

British Library Cataloguing in Publication Data

A CIP record for this book is available from the Public Library

© BILD Publications 2006

BILD Publications is the imprint of:
British Institute of Learning Disabilities
Campion House
Green Street
Kidderminster
Worcestershire DY10 1JL

Telephone: 01562 723010
Fax: 01562 723029
E-mail: enquiries@bild.org.uk

Website: www.bild.org.uk

ISBN 1 904082 97 1

BILD publications are distributed by:
BookSource
32 Finlas Street
Cowlairs Estate
Glasgow G22 5DU

Telephone: 08702 402182
Fax: 0141 5770189

For a publications catalogue with details of all BILD books and journals
telephone 01562 723010, e-mail enquiries@bild.org.uk or visit the
BILD website: www.bild.org.uk

Printed in the UK by Latimer Trend & Company Ltd, Plymouth

About the British Institute of Learning Disabilities

The British Institute of Learning Disabilities is committed to improving the quality of life for people with a learning disability by involving them and their families in all aspects of our work, working with government and public bodies to achieve full citizenship, undertaking beneficial research and development projects and helping service providers to develop and share good practice.

Acknowledgements

I'd like to thank everyone who assisted me with this book by sharing their ideas, opinions and experiences with me. In particular I wish to thank Alice Drife, David Weir and Tricia Connolly. Also thanks to BILD for their support and to my sister Helen. I am most grateful to all of you.

About the author

Alice Bradley is a freelance trainer and consultant and an Open University tutor. She has worked with people with learning disabilities of all ages, as well as families and professionals, for many years in schools, urban and rural communities and higher education establishments in the UK and several countries in Asia and Africa. She is currently undertaking work for BILD, the Scottish Consortium for Learning Disability and the Scottish Qualifications Authority. She is the author of many books on learning disabilities.

Contents

Introduction

This book is intended for managers and senior practitioners concerned with support services for people with learning disabilities who want to continue their professional development. It should also be of interest to senior staff and managers who are preparing for the Learning Disabilities Awards Framework (LDAF) Higher Professional Diploma in Learning Disability Services (Level 4) Unit 3: Personal Development and Reflective Practice in a Learning Disability Service and studying S/NVQ at Level 4.

The purpose of the book is to highlight the importance of reflection in learning and the crucial role of personal and professional development for managers of support services for people with learning disabilities. The issues explored include:

- the principles of reflective practice and personal development

- the learning process and its relevance for personal and professional development

- the values underpinning professional practice in services for people with learning disabilities

- the importance of an integrated approach to practice, which encompasses knowledge of current developments

The book provides readers with the opportunity to evaluate their own progress in learning and development. For LDAF candidates, this will involve an appraisal of their study for the Higher Professional Diploma. For others, it can be applied to similar courses of study. For all readers, it should support continuing professional development.

How the book is organised

The book has four chapters:

Chapter 1   Understanding reflective practice, examines the meaning of the term 'reflective practice', provides opportunities for you to reflect on the values underpinning your own practice, identify the influence of reflection and appraise the support available for reflective practice in your own situation.

Chapter 2   Personal development needs and personal development planning, is about the process of personal development planning (PDP), which includes the identification of learning and development needs, strengths and talents, describing development goals and drawing up a personal development plan. This chapter has a bigger number of activities than other chapters because it takes you through a simulated process of development planning.

Chapter 3   Learning and professional development, deals with the implementation of the development plan and explores the learning process, learning styles, monitoring and review. This chapter also provides you with guidance on how to reflect on your own learning by keeping a learning journal.

Chapter 4   Integrating new developments into practice, explores an integrated approach to practice, focusing upon keeping up-to-date with developments, utilising external networks, adopting a critical approach to research findings, evaluating your own action research and implementing research and legislation in your workplace.

Following chapter 4 there are references and a resources section that includes useful contact addresses and suggestions for additional reading.

The LDAF Higher Professional Diploma (Level 4)

The Higher Professional Diploma is intended for managers and senior workers in services supporting adults with learning disabilities, eg supported employment or supported living, residential or respite services, day care and community based support services. There are two pathways to the diploma – Managing Learning Disability Services and Senior Practitioner in Learning Disability Services – each requiring a particular combination of units from the unit bank. Learners need to complete 12 units to achieve the full qualification. Further information is available at www.city-and-guilds.co.uk

Personal Development and Reflective Practice in a Learning Disability Service, the unit addressed in this book, is a mandatory unit for both pathways. All of the topics required for successful completion of this unit are covered. The aims and outcomes of this LDAF unit are listed below.

Aims

This unit aims to enable the learner to:

● explore the principles of reflective practice and personal development

● consider the learning process and its impact on practice and values

● apply these factors to the current learning programme

Outcomes

On successful completion of this unit the learner will be able to:

● understand the principles of reflective practice

● analyse personal development needs and how to address them

● evaluate the learning process

● integrate new developments into practice

Non-diploma readers

For readers not undertaking the LDAF diploma the book serves as a stand-alone text which contributes to Continuing Professional Development (CPD) or assists towards a qualification other than LDAF.

Activities and reflections

At intervals throughout the book you will be asked to undertake activities or reflections. It's important that you do this, as such engagement with the material helps you apply your learning to your own practice. Some of the information will probably be familiar to you, but it is always useful to revisit old haunts, not least because continuous reflection leads to deeper learning. These reflections also help you prepare for your assignment if you are a LDAF candidate. You might also find some of the activities, and the outcomes of your own reflections, useful as the basis for discussion at staff meetings or for staff supervision purposes.

The advisory and support group

The British Institute of Learning Disabilities' commitment to keeping in close touch with current practice is reflected in the voices of the people who assisted with this book by sharing their opinions and experiences with me and who constituted my advisory and support group. Their input is represented by both direct quotations and in the overall content.

Chapter 1

Understanding reflective practice

Introduction

It isn't often that you get the opportunity to turn the spotlight on yourself, but that's what this book asks you to do. This isn't pure indulgence but an opportunity to consider your own personal and professional development and reflect upon your own practice – probably something you don't always get much time to do, as one manager remarked:

'I think that personal development has a degree of guilt involved because I think that if you are taking time to develop yourself you feel there is something, even as basic as reading, you should be doing instead. I think that it is hard sometimes just to say that, OK, I'm going to read for an hour and read something, you know, that is related to your work. I don't think it happens as often as it should do and I think that you always kind of feel that if you're reading you're not working and that you could go and work at something because there is always something to work at. So I think that part of the trouble I have is trying to do that. I think personal development is really difficult and that sometimes what we do is try to develop the individuals who work for us and, probably more often than not, you need somebody to develop you – you need somebody to look at you and say, right, OK, how are we going to develop you? Because I'm not very good at doing that. I think that you do develop professionally and personally with some of the work experience you have and can take those skills into other things – but only if you have the opportunity.'

The LDAF outline for this unit echoes this sentiment, saying that it: 'covers an aspect of working that is vital to the well-being of a service, but which can easily be overlooked in the business of day-to-day activity. It concerns the personal development of those who hold responsibility at a senior level.

The needs of many groups and individuals compete for attention in a support service, and it can be difficult to give priority to keeping one's own knowledge and practice up to date. But it is an essential activity...' (LDAF unit descriptor).

You will probably agree.

I begin the book with this chapter about reflective practice, which I feel is a particularly relevant topic given its reliance on you as a manager or senior practitioner and on the experience you have acquired through the varied experience such a position provides. I explore:

- what we mean by 'reflective practice'

- why reflective practice is important in professional life

- how you can develop your own capacity as a reflective practitioner

- the implications of reflective practice for you and the service you work in

- support that facilitates reflective practice

What is meant by 'reflective practice'?

Maich, Brown and Royle (2000) point out that there are numerous definitions of reflection and reflective practice. I've selected a few for comparison in the first activity.

ACTIVITY 1: **What is 'reflective practice'?**

Read the following definitions of reflective practice and then answer the questions that follow.

'Reflective practice involves thinking about and learning from your own practice and from the practices of others so as to gain new perspectives on the dilemmas and contradictions inherent in your ... situation, improve judgement, and increase the probability of taking informed action when situations are complex, unique and uncertain' (Center for Support of Teaching and Learning at Syracuse University, NY www.cstl.syr.edu).

'Reflective practice is a mode that integrates or links thought and action with reflection. It involves thinking about and critically analyzing one's actions with the goal of improving one's professional practice. Engaging in reflective practice requires individuals to assume the perspective of an external observer in order to identify the assumptions and feelings underlying their practice and then to speculate about how these assumptions and feelings affect practice' (www.ericdigests.org/1992-3/adult.htm).

'Reflection is an essential step in the lifelong process of learning from our personal and professional experiences...Reflection is particularly valued in the context of a professional life because of its potential to enhance learning while we are in the midst of professional practice' (Watson and Wilcox, 2000, p.58).

'Reflective practice is a way of acting that allows people to look rigorously and productively at the ways in which they support their tasks, the way they collaborate with people, and the ways in which they form assumptions, draw conclusions and selectively attend to certain portions of 'reality.'

Reflective practice gives us tools to get underneath our assumptions, and conventional knowledge, to see the world anew. We can reframe or revise the ways we interpret our experience of our workplace and the world' (www2.fhs.usyd.edu.au/arow/o/mo8/what.htm).

Can you see any common threads running through these definitions?

How do they differ?

How do these definitions of reflective practice compare with your own understanding of it?

Comment

For similarities, I noted that thinking, learning and action are interlinked – either specified or implied; that *critical* thinking is necessary and that change is either specified or implied.

But I also noted that most definitions focused on learning from your own practice, while you talked about your own and other people's. Also, there were different emphases, eg some people stressed underlying assumptions.

The debate about reflective practice continues and will probably do so for a long time. Clouder and Sellars (2004) write: 'it is evident in the literature that reflective practice has been adopted across a wide range of professions in the absence of thorough knowledge or debate about its underpinning philosophy, or even consensus about its processes, purpose or benefits in terms of learning (Morrison, 1995; Clarke et al, 1996; Clouder, 2000)' (p. 263).

Florez (2001) emphasises the fact that reflective practice is an evolving concept that has been influenced by various philosophical and pedagogical theories, among them: 'constructivism, which views learning as an active process where learners reflect upon their current and past knowledge and experiences to generate new ideas and concepts. A *humanistic* element ... (which) is its concern with personal growth and its goal of liberation from values that can limit growth (Kullman, 1998). *Critical pedagogy*, espousing examination of underlying power bases and struggles...' (p. 1).

There are similarities here with Leitch and Day's (2000) reference to a *continuum of reflective practice*. These authors contend that there has been too much emphasis on the rational and cognitive aspects of reflective practice and not enough on the underlying values, attitudes and emotions that have considerable influence on what we do in practice. These writers support a holistic view of reflective practice, arguing that: 'while a reflective practitioner may be concerned to improve practice and to develop additional competence, what defines the effective reflective practitioner is more a set of attitudes towards practice based upon broader understandings of self, society and moral purposes than those which seek simply to increase efficiency in relation to 'deliver' and narrowly conceived achievement targets' (p. 181).

I asked one manager about her thoughts on the role of feelings in reflection.

Me: Some people say that reflective practice has become too technical and too intellectualised and that we don't pay enough attention to our feelings when we reflect. I wonder whether we have to some extent lost sight of the importance of the feelings and the person. What do you think?

Manager: I think that I very much operate from a feeling point – it's something that, over the years doing a lot of work on myself, I became personally aware of. Doing the SVQ and having gone through that and having to give evidence of the practice element in order to actually obtain the unit, to get the qualification, it didn't change how I did it, it didn't change. Some of the units that are value based units, then you have to evidence the person you are, and your feelings have to come into that. I felt really comfortable writing like this. …and so our assessor got to know us as people and got a sense of the bits … of us as people, and the feelings that might have underpinned the decisions we were putting in as evidence. I don't feel that in our case that was lost, but I suppose I could see a danger where it could be if it became purely a functional, academic exercise.

This wide perspective on reflective practice is good news, I believe, because it indicates that reflective practice is a dynamic process that enables you to think not only about your own practice (what you do and how you do it) but the underpinning values, beliefs and theories you bring to your work, and to the social, political and economic context within which you operate, both in your own services and organisation and in society. In other words, it reflects the realities of working life. What we often refer to as 'gut feeling' is, in fact, based on years of experience that has become embedded in our individual practice. Reflection can help us uncover the learning which occurred as a result of these experiences and capitalise upon it.

Reflective practice enables you to:

- explore your own underlying values and beliefs and recognise the ways in which these affect your own approach to practice

- identify the ways in which your emotions influence your work practice

- explore the relationships between your own behaviour and problem situations

- identify contradictions and dilemmas within your own practice, eg behaving in ways contrary to what you profess to believe

- understand perspectives other than your own

- explore the influence of context in problem situations, eg systems, structures and policies within or external to the service in which you work

- learn from reflection and integrate this learning within your practice on an ongoing basis

The origins of reflective practice

Reflection is something most of us do naturally. We frequently replay events and interactions in our minds: 'What if I'd said…', 'I should have…' 'I wonder what he thought of the way I…' – and so on. It's a good start, but reflective practice is much more than just rethinking experiences. Essentially, it's about the knowledge and understanding we build up through our own experience, and that of others, in the *professional* sphere as opposed to what are often referred to as the 'technical' aspects of our job, ie the theories and techniques we learn through more formal training. Reflective practice is based on the premise that we construct meanings within the situations we experience and that our values, attitudes and emotions, as well as previous experience, knowledge and understanding, shape these meanings. So, for example, two or more people involved in the same interaction will interpret the situation differently according to what governs their individual perspectives.

Reflective practice probably has its origins well in the past, but it is names such as John Dewey and, most notably, Donald Schon that are most commonly associated with its emergence as a recognised theory. Dewey was primarily a philosopher with a particular interest in learning. His work on thinking, problem solving, learning and reflection informed many subsequent theories. He defined reflective thought as 'active, persistent and careful consideration of any belief or supposed form of knowledge in the light of the grounds that support it and further conclusions to which it tends' (1933, p. 118) and more recently, reflection as 'the kind of thinking that consists of turning a subject over in the mind and giving it serious and consecutive consideration'.

Dewey's writings influenced the work of Donald Schon (1930–97), who had a particular interest in effectiveness in practice. Schon's well-known book, *The Reflective Practitioner* (1983), based upon analysis of practice across different professions (Altrichter, Posch and Somekh, 1993), has given rise to much of what happens today in relation to reflective practice. Like Dewey, Schon believed that people learn by doing. Professional thinking, he contended, should be based not only on the application of established theory, but also on knowledge gained from experience and on non-logical types of thinking about what is relevant and appropriate in particular contexts (Yoong, 1999).

Schon's work was a reaction against what he considered to be overdependence on the technical aspects of a profession, ie the application of theory to the solution of a problem as opposed to the knowledge and understanding that is built up through the experience of being a professional and working in the real and constantly changing world in a number of different contexts. His concern was with professional learning and the relationships between professional knowledge and professional action. He highlighted the importance of 'an epistemology of practice' as 'necessary to characterise professional know-how and action' (Clegg, 2000, p. 451).

Three aspects of Schon's discussions on professional knowledge and practice are particularly relevant for an understanding of this epistemology of practice. He called these *tacit knowing-in-action, reflection-in-action* and *reflection-on-action*.

Tacit knowing-in-action is based on aspects of professional practice that appear to be instinctive. Schon wrote: 'When we go about the spontaneous, intuitive performance of the actions of everyday life, we show ourselves to be knowledgeable in a special way. Often we cannot say what it is that we know. When we try to describe it we find ourselves at a loss, or we produce descriptions that are obviously inappropriate. Our knowledge is ordinarily tacit, implicit in our patterns of action and in our feel for the stuff with which we are dealing. Similarly, the workday life of the professional depends on tacit-knowing-in-action' (1983, p. 49).

According to Schon, in this type of practice, thinking and action are not separate and we are often unaware of where our knowledge has come from. The knowing is inherent in the action. In reality, the knowledge which enables us to practise so adeptly has been acquired somehow – it constitutes a professional 'know-how' which we have built up through experience and which enables us to perform effectively in a wide range of situations and contexts. As we become more experienced, *knowing-in-action* about all kinds of professional activities becomes more deeply embedded in our work practices. This kind of action is sometimes referred to as intuitive.

However, there are times when we encounter new situations or particular problems in familiar situations. Then it is not enough to respond spontaneously or in the way we usually do. We must 'think on our feet', bringing our professional knowledge to bear. Schon calls this kind of thinking *reflection-in-action*. The professional, he says, becomes a researcher in the practice context, trying to fathom or 'frame' the problem and find ways of dealing with it, using on-the-spot experimentation. The framing of the problem is as crucial as resolving it. If the problem is incorrectly framed, the solution tried will be inadequate. In this situation, as professionals, we don't rely on established ideas, techniques or theories. We have to draw on our own knowledge and experience. The thinking is going on at the same time as the action, as opposed to *reflection-on-action* (see p. 21) where reflection is retrospective. This is a crucial element of professional practice where 'reflection-in-action acknowledges the tacit processes of *thinking* which accompany *doing*, and which constantly interact with and modify ongoing practice in such a way that learning takes place' (Leitch and Day, 2000, p. 180). By engaging in *reflection-in-action*, professionals add to their existing knowledge and expertise and, by implication, their own capacities (Altrichter et al, 1993; Silva, www.learning-org.com).

ACTIVITY 2: **Using reflection-in-action**

Can you think of an example of when you encountered a situation that meant you had to employ reflection-in-action? Describe the situation briefly.

Comment

I can't know what you described, obviously, but I'm pretty sure there have been many occasions when you've had to think on your feet and when moment by moment feedback has informed each subsequent action. Responding to someone with challenging behaviour while ensuring that both the person and other people are kept safe is a good example. You may have well-developed strategies for managing challenging behaviour, but there is usually some level of unpredictability involved, as well as individual differences. Skills and knowledge do not necessarily transfer automatically – reflection is a useful tool in such situations.

In discussion, managers of a supported living service highlighted the fact that they need not only to think on their feet but also to take account of changing circumstances. They told me:

'It's so fluid – what's an issue one week isn't always… you know, you can't be prepared for the next – and currently we're supporting a lady who's very, very ill at the end stage of senile dementia. We're also supporting a man who's going into mid-stage – you would think that's transferable learning, but it's so different, and so we have to kind of work from the drawing board and say, well, these are the issues. So it's that constant change in what the local development needs are that I suppose is kind of very difficult to remain on top of. And when you've got the staff team of thirty or forty people…'

'I think the pressure of work sometimes means that the development that you have started is reactive as opposed to proactive – frequently – but that's the nature of the job, you know, because you will be faced with first-time situations – frequently, in 80 per cent of cases – thinking back to like, well, maybe where a lady that we support began to drink quite a bit. So you're thinking, OK, how do we support the team to deal with that? Because people were coming and saying, "look, this is what happened when we were supporting that person". So you're saying, OK, let's look at what we can do within this situation. So you very quickly put together something in terms of risk assessment and also giving people knowledge, and giving people an understanding of what are the boundaries of their role and putting all of those things together, in response to something that happened.'

Schon's third concept, *reflection-on-action*, applies to situations when we need to make our knowledge explicit so that we can understand it better, learn from it and apply this learning to future practice. We distance ourselves from the situation and then reflect upon it. This is what we generally mean when we talk about being a reflective practitioner – conscious reflection in which we think about and analyse an aspect of practice, including, most crucially, the underlying processes and influences. Distancing ourselves from the action enables us to take a more objective stance, redefine the problem more accurately and identify any contradictions between what we profess to believe and how we behave. This type of reflection also helps us to become more aware of the 'tacit knowledge' referred to in *knowing-in-action* (Altrichter et al, 1993). It is retrospective analysis which makes available to the practitioner knowledge based on experience (Leitch and Day, 2000).

There have been many criticisms of Schon's theories, most notably in relation to lack of clarity and specificity. Clouder and Sellars (2004) refer to 'conceptual ambiguity' (p. 263). Despite all this, Schon's work has been the most influential in relation to reflective practice. Clegg (2000) draws attention to the misuse of Schon's work in 'the achievement of personal and institutional goals (Ecclestone, 1996), rather than Schon's own proposals for a research programme designed to provide insights into the nature of professional knowledge and practice' (p. 452).

The work of Boud, Keogh and Walker (1985) has also had a considerable impact on our understanding of reflective practice. One of their greatest strengths is that they give due consideration to the emotional aspects of practice, considering both *intellectual and affective* activities integral to the exploration of our experiences if we are to achieve new insights. These authors developed a model of reflection in which they identify three stages: returning to the experience, attending to the associated feelings and re-evaluating the experience. This process leads to new perspectives, the application of the new learning and changes in behaviour.

You might like to think about...

...how 'reflective' you are as a manager or senior practitioner and whether any of your reflection is planned. For instance, do you keep a diary about your own practice, 'think things through' on paper or computer, jot down thoughts and ideas? You almost certainly participate – and perhaps lead – shared reflection with colleagues at staff meetings of different kinds.

Why is reflective practice important in professional life?

Reflection is something we do in practice whether we are conscious of it or not. Work with human beings is always complex and often unpredictable. Often we ourselves are not fully aware of why we behave in certain ways. When questioned closely – in supervision, for example – we can often uncover what lies beneath our actions – and learn from it. I work regularly with front-line social care workers, many of whom feel, justifiably, that their perceived status is low and their work undervalued. Many are conscious of their lack of qualifications compared to 'professionals' and they don't always have a great deal of confidence in their own worth as practitioners. They talk about 'using common sense' in support situations. Yet when they are given opportunities to reflect on their own strengths, talents and experiences they begin to realise just how much of a body of knowledge and understanding they have built up, both as individuals and collectively – a true 'professional knowledge'. It's ironic that this type of professionalism is so little valued in our society. Schon challenges the view that professionalism is something you acquire through the transmission of established knowledge in formal training. This 'technical' aspect of the job is important, he acknowledges, but no more so than the learning we acquire through experience and the application of 'self' to every situation we encounter. Reflection enables us to 'expose' this often hidden aspect of our practice, to gain new insight and to build on what we learn, thus enlarging our own body of knowledge. Sharing this knowledge with other professionals adds further perspective and can accelerate learning.

Reflective practice broadens our understanding not only of what we do and why we do it, but also of the wider work, social, economic and political context within which we operate. According to Leitch and Day (2000), 'what defines the effective practitioner is more a set of attitudes towards practice based upon a broader understanding of self, society and moral purposes than those which seek simply to increase efficiency in relation to "delivery" and narrowly conceived achievement targets' (p. 181). Reflection facilitates greater self-knowledge and understanding, fuller personal development and a deeper analysis of our own values, attitudes, beliefs and personal theories. Reflection can help us identify contradictions between what we profess to believe and how we act, while enabling us to understand the constraints and contextual influences which may create or contribute to the dilemmas we experience. For example, in practice we have to reconcile a commitment to empowerment, autonomy and individual freedom for the people who use our services with accountability and risk management. More mundanely, time constraints and workload may cause us to compromise principles we say we firmly believe in. Organisational demands may take precedence over service user rights. Reflection can provide us with a means of exploring such conflicts and finding ways of resolving them. Leitch and Day (2000) highlight the importance of recognising the impact of organisational and cultural contexts on professional growth. Although addressed to teachers, their comments are equally relevant for social care and health professionals.

Reflective practice across professional disciplines is an important aspect of learning about practice. Referring to its use in orthopaedic nursing, Driscoll and Teh (2001) describe reflective practice as the ability of professionals to analyse their own actions and judge their own effectiveness. The process allows the person to uncover the thoughts, feelings and behaviours that are present in particular incidences. By so doing they discover new types of knowledge that is embedded in practice and can challenge existing knowledge from 'those often "outside practice" and evaluate this in relation to other forms of knowledge from within, the "real world"' (p. 97). This, they believe, enhances rather than competes with existing knowledge, enhances the value of practice, improves service quality and generates knowledge based on real practice. Gustafsson and Fagerberg (2004), in a study of the use of reflection by nurses in their daily work, found that the experiences helped those involved to develop and mature professionally, to recognise the uniqueness of each person they cared for, to achieve greater empathy, to take account of ethical considerations and to recognise the effects of power structures on their work practice. This knowledge enabled them to make better use of supervision, to move beyond traditional boundaries and try something new, and to develop the courage needed to challenge inequalities.

Clegg (2000) is sceptical of some of the ways in which reflective practice is currently used, pointing out that, in some situations, reflection has become a way of 'inculcating required normative attitudes rather than a practice that attempts to look critically at the self and the world' (p. 452). Boud and Walker (1998) warn against intellectualising reflection, adopting a 'recipe' approach, reflection without learning and a belief that reflection can be easily contained. They emphasise the importance of a state of perplexity, hesitation or doubt and the need to confront discomfort and dilemmas as well as to explore uncertainty, discrepancy and dissatisfaction. None of this comes easily to us as professionals. After all, the expectation often is that we are the 'experts' with the answers. Letting go of this traditional model of professionalism and entering into exploratory relationships with other colleagues, let alone service users and their families, is disconcerting and takes a considerable amount of professional maturity and confidence.
Yet it opens many doors to much deeper learning. It enables us to adopt new perspectives, explore continuously, appraise our own performance and find better ways of serving the people we support. And it's reassuring.

ACTIVITY 3: **Your feelings about reflective practice**

Bearing in mind the points made by the writers I've mentioned above, list three ways you think reflective practice will be most useful to you in your current job role.

What do you consider is most challenging about being a reflective practitioner in your current job role?

Comment

Reflection enhances our ability to be in charge of our own practice, rather than having ideas and opinions imposed upon us. By gaining deeper insight into our professional and personal selves and understanding how the two interact and contribute towards our work practice, we establish a stronger sense of self, both personal and professional. We become more confident, which enables us to deal with challenge and to challenge ourselves, to change our ideas and perspectives, to be open to different ways of doing things and comfortable in dealing with the contradictions and complexity of our professional life. Did any of these points feature in the first part of your answer?

The challenging part isn't difficult to identify, is it? Time, a heavy workload, the unpredictability of working with other human beings, managerial responsibilities, trying to reconcile the needs of the people your service supports with the demands of the organisation, statutory authorities and so on – you probably thought of several others. Which means that we need to find ways of building reflection in as integral and manageable aspects of practice. To do this we need support from the organisation and a climate that encourages reflection.

How can you develop your own capacity as a reflective practitioner?

So how do you become a reflective practitioner? The starting point is that you already *are* one – as you are well aware. When you think about issues, sit down with colleagues to try to find solutions to problems, listen to carers unhappy with some aspect of the service, you engage in reflection as a matter of habit. Sometimes there are practical or technical solutions to a problem, but not always. The key is to make use of your existing capacities as a reflective practitioner and develop these further.

A crucial role of reflective practice is to uncover the assumptions, values and theories that underpin your actions in practice. It's relatively easy to develop policies that extol the importance of empowerment for people with learning disabilities and emphasise equality, rights and anti-discriminative practice. However, when we start to reflect on our own practice, we often discover that what we *say* and what we *do* conflict. There are many reasons for this, eg the systems and structures of the service, external forces, such as legislation or government policy or priorities. Some arise from within ourselves: paying lip-service to certain beliefs; not being as aware as we should be of our own value systems; not thinking through what we do, or assessing whether our actions are compatible with our professed values and attitudes. We might, for example, say we believe in people's right to make their own mistakes and control their own futures, yet adopt a protective approach towards them. Or consider our practice to be empowering, yet find out that it is really fostering dependency. As managers, what we consider 'supportive' might in fact be controlling and prevent people developing their own capacity.

Use the next activity to explore this issue.

Activity 4: **Exploring contradictions in practice and values**

Read the examples and then answer the questions that follow.

First example
Rene is employed as a development worker for a self-advocacy group. She gets on well with the group members and they obviously like her and value her opinion. She takes an active part in their meetings and often suggests ways of campaigning which will challenge aspects of community life which members find discriminatory, eg access to public transport, having information provided in accessible ways. When you meet Rene it is obvious that she is one of the group and identifies closely with them and their aspirations. You'll often see her out with one or more of the group members, buying the train tickets or organising lunch. She is obviously committed to what she is doing and says she likes 'getting her teeth into things'. She is very vocal and often comments on the inequalities and injustices disabled people face. When you address one of the group members, he or she usually looks towards Rene for support and she often answers for the person, adding things like, 'Didn't you?' or 'Do you remember we went to the job centre to talk to them about writing things in simpler language?'

Questions
From this short description what contradictions can you identify between Rene's practice and the values and principles that should underpin her practice?

If you were Rene's supervisor how would you encourage reflection to help her recognise and tackle these contradictions?

How could such reflection help her resolve these contradictions?

Second example

Angela is a manager of a housing service for people with learning disabilities and has responsibility for 15 support workers, five senior support workers and two deputy managers. She is totally committed to the principles of the service, eg tenants' rights, equality, promoting autonomy while providing support, person centred planning, empowerment and so on.

She likes to stay up-to-date with what staff are doing and often says she 'runs a tight ship'. Staff seem divided in the extent to which they get along with her. Some really like her, depend on her a lot and keep her well informed about what they are doing. She is sympathetic towards their personal problems and likes to help and support them and make allowances if they need time off and so on. Others tend to steer clear of her and consider her concern for their personal lives as intrusive. They also feel that she has her favourites and doesn't treat everyone equally. She disputes this, pointing out that she needs to know that she can depend on 'her' staff and that some staff are more reliable and responsive than others, so she treats them accordingly. Recently she has had to give a verbal warning to a member of staff she feels isn't pulling his weight and this has divided the staff team even further. Both her deputies – a man and a woman – are fully supportive of her and are good friends.

Questions

What contradictions can you identify between the underlying principles of the service and the way Angela deals with the staff?

How could reflection help Angela improve her practice as a manager?

What impact would you hope this would have on the staff team?

How could this improve the service for tenants?

Comment

You can only work on the limited information I've provided, of course. But even so you can see that Rene has, probably unknowingly, caused people in the group to become too dependent on her. It's good that they have a collective identity as a group and feel supported by her, but I'd question the extent to which they are truly developing their own capacities to advocate for themselves, their own personalities or empowering themselves, wouldn't you?

In the second example, Angela seems to be operating according to mixed principles, having some rules for some staff and some for others according to her own feelings about them. If she believes in equality, empowerment and the other service principles, these should be reflected in her management of staff, as well as service users. A divided staff group cannot provide a supportive service.

Reflection can help you challenge your own practice, identify contradictions and discover how those contradictions might have arisen.

Reflection can also help you:

- develop insight into why things happen and which factors – personal, service and external – influence events and your own practice

- discern patterns in your own practice, both positive and negative

- identify your own strengths, talents, skills, needs and gaps in knowledge and understanding

- develop your own questioning ability which will enable you to get beneath the surface of your own practice

- generate different options and strategies for dealing with problems and issues in practice situations

- share your perspectives with colleagues and learn from theirs

Challenging your own values and practice

Reflection is a powerful way of challenging both your own *values* and your own *practice*. The first step is to understand and pursue the skills involved in reflection.

McGill and Beaty (2001), drawing on the work of other writers (Habermas, 1974; Argyris and Schon, 1978; Schon, 1983; Boud et al, 1985; and Senge, 1990) have identified some of the skills involved in reflection. These include:

- being able to associate new information with existing information, seeking relationships in data, validating the authenticity of ideas and feelings and making the knowledge our own (Boud et al, 1985)

- slowing down our thinking processes to become more aware of our mental models, ie 'images, assumptions, stories we carry in our heads about people, families, organisations' (p. 181), and about how these influence us (Senge, 1990)

- recognising the gaps between 'espoused theories' (what we profess to believe) and 'theories in use' (the implied theory in what we do and which we are not always conscious of using) (Argyris and Schon, 1978)

- recognising 'leaps of abstraction' (Senge, 1990), ie making generalisations on the basis of very little information, which causes us to form opinions and adopt certain perspectives that may be ill-founded

- drawing attention to what we really think but do not say

- balancing enquiry and advocacy, ie being able to let go of the inclination to defend our own position and perspective (Senge, 1990)

- being able to 'detach' part of ourselves in order to look at another part of self (Habermas, 1974)

In addition, reflection is about:

- recognising the process as a dynamic one, not about being passive and just looking back, but about showing us a way into the future

- understanding other ideas and other people's ways of interpreting the world

- being curious and prepared to ask all types of questions of yourself

- being patient, not jumping to conclusions and not looking for easy answers

- being open to what is happening

- being honest with yourself about doubts, uncertainty and gaps in understanding

- taking account of behaviour, ideas and feelings and discovering how these relate to and interact with one another

- being prepared for uncertainty, doubt and challenge

(http://www.herts.ac.uk/tli/HILP/gradskill/selfmanage/skillreflect.pdf)

Reflection that remains superficial or mechanistic is not true reflection. The purpose is to get beneath our actions to discover what motivates and influences us, both internally and externally. Practice and values are intertwined. 'Value talk' is very common in our profession. Respect, dignity, rights, empowerment, autonomy – they're easy to rhyme off, but more difficult to get hold of, make explicit or assess. I can think of many instances when I've wanted to say to people, 'Excuse me, your values are showing.' I'm sure you can too. Equally, there are times when my own values have been challenged by others. Taking your own values out and having a good look at them isn't easy, so we have to find ways of doing this. This is also true when it comes to our own practice.

Strategies for challenging our own values and practices constructively

At this point I want to explore some of the ways in which reflection can prove particularly productive in helping us challenge our own values and practice.

Reflecting with others

An exploration of the values that underpin our work practice can be done individually, or with one or more other people. Both have advantages and disadvantages. Atherton (2003) comments: 'it can be argued that "real" reflective practice needs another person as mentor or professional supervisor who can ask appropriate questions to ensure that the reflection goes somewhere and does not get bogged down in self-justification, self-indulgence or self-pity' (p. 1).

Hunt (2001) highlights the importance of recognising your own preferred way of thinking. She describes the benefits of reflecting with colleagues when developing a module on reflection in a Masters degree programme in a university in the north of England. She makes a lot of use of metaphors, explaining that this enables her to 'transfer feelings into a space beyond my personal "gut reaction" where I can then begin to explore, explain, and sometimes share them' (p. 276). You can probably think of many occasions when you have used metaphors in your own work, eg 'Look out – she's gunning for everyone today' or 'He looks really lost this weather.' Sometimes, if we allow ourselves to think what lies behind a metaphor we can uncover really useful information, such as feelings and unconscious insights. Hunt identifies some of the ways she has benefited from reflecting on practice, eg a better understanding of how she represents the world to herself and of her own thinking processes, the ability to see familiar things differently, opportunities to seek direction, to 'name' and re-examine experiences and practices and to challenge her own perspective. Reflection with, and challenges from, her colleagues have enabled her to acknowledge 'the validity of a completely different interpretation of my role in certain events' (p. 282).

Cook (2004) reports on six projects which used a variety of 'action research/ reflective practitioner' approaches in a 'New Labour area-based policy initiative' (p. 77) for families and young children. Participants met together regularly as a reflective practice group with an experienced facilitator to support one another and engage in in-depth discussion about their projects. They used different techniques in their projects, including video for observation, diary recording, focus group meetings and interviews and questionnaires. Reflection enabled participants to recognise the influence of their own understandings and perspectives, the nature and origins of their own beliefs, their strengths 'but also the highly personal and contextual basis of their views, beliefs and practices' (p. 86). Through reflection, people became more confident in their own identity and abilities, learned to understand and value other perspectives more, deal with multiple, changing perspectives, construct understandings with others and developed more critical awareness of their own practice. In her summary of the experience, the author raises salient questions about an issue that is particularly pertinent to managers: working with others 'from multiple professional perspectives' (to which we might also add the perspectives of service users and their families). She stresses the importance of understanding what working together really means, eg addressing entrenched behaviours, a supportive workplace ethos and the need for managerial and administrative structures which support a culture of change and innovation.

You might like to think about...

...whether you have sufficient opportunities for meeting together with other professionals for shared reflection

...whether, if you don't already use shared reflection in your service, you could introduce it

...how supportive your work culture is for reflective practice

---

Reflecting in action

Watson and Wilcox (2000) advocate the use of reflection while we are in the midst of professional practice. (Remember Schon's *reflection-in-action*?). Stopping to think and asking ourselves questions like: 'What professional role am I playing at the moment?', 'Why do/did I do that?' and 'What do such moments mean to me and others?' enable us to 'gain insight into universal and particular aspects of our work' (p. 58). Watson and Wilcox talk of *reading in new ways to gain understanding* and suggest that one way of doing this is through reflecting on the 'stories' we tell. We all tell stories, whether or not we are conscious of doing this. When we recount an event, then ask for a colleague's opinion or insight, eg 'I'd like to have a word with you about ...' or 'Did you hear what happened to ...?' or 'What do you think about...?' we are telling a story. Storytelling happens more formally in meetings and has a variety of purposes. Approaches such as person centred planning are based on people's stories. In my story, I describe my 'reading' of a situation and you describe yours. We might then explore similarities and differences, ask questions, seek clarification and explore our feelings, among other things. In so doing, we arrive at a new understanding of the situation, not necessarily at that time, but possibly later. If I am entrenched in my opinion or perspective and you in yours little or no learning takes place for either of us because we are not willing to explore our differences and what lies beneath them. You know the sort of thing – 'We've tried that and it doesn't work'; 'I've heard all this before'; 'We've been doing this for years' and suchlike. Learning requires openness and respect for one another. Storytelling (narrative) is an established and respected way of researching situations and has a long history.

An example of reflection and storytelling was recounted by a tenant in a supported living service. She explained how staff and tenants get together regularly to review people's feelings about the service and make the necessary changes. People talk about their individual concerns and also give collective views on how things could improve:

'Well, like the tenants' handbook, it's far too big and full of jargon words. So we said how do you think tenants can understand it, so they said well what can we do about it and we said we could make it easier and put pictures in it – like graphics and things. And that's what we did – it's just this size now [indicating a very thin document with her thumb and forefinger]. We've done that with all the other documents too. They know better now and it was the tenants that did it.'

She also told me how the 'storytelling' in the group led to a change in the way support was provided:

'It's just that one support worker used to have a group. We could only see our key worker once a week, but that was in a great big group. How the heck are you supposed to talk to your key worker in private if there's another nine people there? Now we've still got the group but we've got a lot of one-to-one meetings as well. It's a lot better.'

Reflection and the written word

Watson and Wilcox (2000) suggest what they call 'collecting and reading the conventions of practice' (p. 63) to aid reflection. They suggest that we can gain insight into these conventions by a 'reading' of the documentation and 'artefacts' (videos, photographs, etc) we create. In practice this could mean looking at the written documents we create, such as letters, memos, policy documents and so on.

We can look at:

- the purpose of the different documents and the likely or actual effect on the people reading them

- how inclusive or exclusive documents are, how accessible and how important or significant. For example, we can 'read between the lines' and learn more about what underpins our own practice

- the tone and the language we use, eg is it respectful of everyone, does it value the people it is addressed to, or abrupt and unfriendly, or dictatorial? I'm sure, like me, you can think of times when you were inundated with paper or e-mails, many unnecessary. Is there some correspondence you pay particular attention to because you know it will be important? Are there e-mails and memos which make you bristle with indignation or annoyance because they are demanding, discourteous and/or imperious? Most importantly, we need to ask ourselves if we are ever guilty of any of this

---

You might like to...

...have a look at 'the written word' in your organisation, eg memos and e-mails, notices around the place, letters written by people in the service (including yourself) and sent to the service. What kind of picture do they present?

What about any photographs or pictures displayed?

In the outpatients department of a general hospital I visit I'm always struck by the 'staff on duty' list on the noticeboard. Doctors are listed by title and surnames, nurses by first names only. Once I asked about this discrepancy and a staff nurse told me, 'It's only for patients. We can address the doctors by their first names.' Somehow I felt he'd missed my point. Are you, like me, conscious of notices in shops – the ones that say 'Don't touch!' and those that say 'Please touch'? And in community meeting places how welcoming are the notices or how forbidding and controlling? How we express ourselves in writing speaks volumes. How we handle and transmit information is also highly indicative – information is definitely power. How empowering, accessible and inclusive are the documents you create?

Using diaries or journals for reflection

One of the most frequently used strategies in reflective practice is that of the journal or diary. Rothwell and Ghelipter (2003) describe the use of reflective diaries with undergraduate management students in the UK and Israel. They found that students needed very clear and repeated guidance on the production of their diaries if they were to get beyond the level of mere description, but report that those who engaged well with the process were more focused, better able to articulate their range of feelings and to achieve deep, rather than surface learning. Altrichter et al (1993) recommend the diary format as a means of recording insights and ideas. They stress that diary writing is very personal and that we all have our own styles and idiosyncrasies, which are extremely important. People not used to diary writing may find it challenging at first, but the process can be invaluable if you persevere through the initial difficult period. On a practical level, loose-leaf binders make it easier to insert additional insights and information, as do wide margins. Some sort of structure, such as headings and sub-headings can be helpful, but not everyone likes to use them. Dating entries is important to help you keep track of developments. For a diary to be truly reflective, it needs to include feelings, observations, reactions, ideas and explanations, not just descriptive or factual data. Photographs and graphics also help.

In chapter 2 I discuss the use of reflective diaries or journals in relation to progress through personal and professional development, especially with regard to reviewing your own learning.

Concluding comment

Reflection is an integral part of professional development. It may be something you already do in a planned way, but you almost certainly use it informally as an ongoing aspect of your practice.

Here are some extracts from my discussions with managers of an organisation which provides supported living for people with learning disabilities. They explained how they usually engage in reflection, not always consciously or deliberately:

'I think reflecting on how you improve yourself and your own skills and abilities is important. My own example is that when throughout the day, when I am working on things, different things come up and I think, 'How could I have done that better?' Not every situation is the same, even if you think it's the same you are going to do that because you work with people all the time. People are different, you treat them individually. You might think the system allows me to do this, this and this – but why can't I do this, this and this? In this case there is another context and so you reflect on that and think, OK, that would improve that situation, or I could have done that better. It's about improving yourself and improving the service you offer – and it's also about looking at building your knowledge. You're thinking from the big picture to how that fits here and that reflects on your knowledge, on how you've kept yourself up to date.'

'I think it's about, sometimes, just stopping for an instant. I would like to think it is something that is a part of who I am anyway. But I think sometimes it's when you're going full speed ahead with things and you're not really thinking about, you know, what you want to achieve out of a particular piece of work, and you know you have to get it done by the end of the day because you've got something else to do tomorrow, and you kind of run with it – for me it's about sometimes stopping to think, well, do I actually need to run with this today? Why am I doing it? Am I doing it just to get it out the way? Is the timing right? I can sometimes have a bit more awareness and I do try to do that consciously. In doing the SVQ, you were always looking for evidence in practice that you could write to, so you get into that way of thinking – Why am I doing this? Does it need to be done like this? Whereas I wouldn't have questioned that so much in the past. I would probably have just done it.'

'It's maybe not always the most conscious thing in your mind. But I think, having come back from an 11-day holiday with two service users, I thought I was one of the only people who could go there, to support those two people, because I thought that it was someone with my skills and my abilities who was needed to do that. Having been on the holiday, and the type of holiday it is, coming back and realising I never personally go on that type of holiday, I now question if those two men got as much out of that holiday as they could have done if they'd gone with someone who does go on that kind of holiday. I really do now, and it's been quite difficult wondering about that. I don't think it detracted from the person's holiday enormously. They had a good time and I think there was plenty evidence of this – it was well organised and it went smoothly, and not having any stress for the people who were there, because that was part of the exercise, because they wanted a break to be relaxed – all of those things happened. But at the same time every night there was entertainment on at the hotel. By 11 o'clock I was desperate to go to bed to read my book – that's me, that is who I am, whereas it wasn't necessarily what those two people wanted. I wasn't reflective like that before (I've been on lots of holidays before) and I probably didn't bring that level of reflection to it. So I am thinking, Did I actually need to be there? Was it in the best interest of the service for me to be there? Or could the people have been supported... you're caught between a rock and a hard place because the alternative was sending two relief registered workers, people who work for us on a regular basis, or a very inexperienced support worker, weighing up the risks involved – and you are very conscious that if you ask those people to participate in that and it goes wrong, the responsibility is still yours. But I have made the decision that I am almost certainly not the right person to go back, as long as we get the other bits right.'

'I find myself at times taking on bits of work, thinking if the work doesn't get done, I should do it. Then I think, I shouldn't have done that, I should have given it to someone else to do because it probably would have been done by now. But I thought that I was the person who had to, or who should or could, do it. And I think it is about trying to be more aware in those situations – thinking, is this the only way of doing it? Am I the person who should be doing it?'

'You can buy into that. I know I get frustrated because people feel I should know everything. But then I ask why do they think that? It's probably because I leap in and do what needs to be done – you set yourself up for it. I am more aware of that as well. I didn't get involved in the committee (to fundraise) because I knew I didn't have the time. But two years ago I would have said, Yes, I can do that. Maybe it's our responsibility to facilitate the opportunity for others to do it. There has been a bit of learning in that'

In an Australian study of reflection, Gardner (2001) found that social work students' practice benefited most from exposure to new ideas and other people's perspectives, open discussions about their own attitudes and values, exploration of the culture of the course and of broader issues, and a sense of community with other students. This isn't earth-shattering, but my point here is that while we usually have these opportunities in training, we don't always build them in enough to the work situation. Nor do we often take time to consider the true nature of the work culture and its effect on our own practice, although we may have an overall consciousness of it.

In chapter 2 I develop these points by focusing on personal and professional development.

Chapter 2

Personal development needs and personal development planning

Introduction

Professional development has always been important in organisations. One manager told me: 'Continuing professional development is important obviously for self-knowledge and experience, and also in relation to staff that I am working with so that I can show them a good role model – also for the quality of the service.'

In this chapter I discuss an approach to professional development called personal development planning (PDP) that is becoming increasingly popular in the UK. This is a process for analysing your own personal and professional development needs and finding ways of addressing them.

Tamkin, Barber and Hirsh (1995) point out that, while PDP is not new, there seems to have been a rapid increase in the numbers of organisations using it over recent years.

It features prominently in universities, for example, for both staff and students, through the efforts of the Quality Assurance Agency for Higher Education (QAA) which, following the National Committee of Enquiry into Higher Education (the Dearing Report) in 1997, highlighted the need for: 'structured and supported processes to develop the capacity of individuals to reflect upon their own learning and achievement, and to plan for their own personal educational and career development' adding: 'The term Personal Development Planning (PDP) is used to denote this process' (1999).

PDP also has a high profile in all sectors of the National Health Service (NHS). For example, two papers from the Scottish Executive, *Towards a New Way of Working* (April 1998) and *Learning Together* (December 1999), highlight the importance of education, development and lifelong learning for all staff within NHS services, setting out a national strategy for staff support. The NHS Knowledge and Skills Framework, part of the strategy for the development of organisations and the workforce, requires the development of a personal development plan (PDP) for all employees in which learning and development needs and interests are identified and pursued: 'You should have gained new knowledge and skills – and developed yourself. And you should be better able to apply your knowledge and skills to your work.'

Professional development is not necessarily about attending a certain number of courses or so many hours of training. One manager said:

'It's not just about formal training and things like that because we do a lot of group work. For example, just now, if we recognise that there is a need to sort of improve something we will maybe set up a working group or something on that and bring in people that are not just the team leaders but support staff or whatever. Another thing is what we're doing with person centred planning is both at regional and local level – there are different staff at different levels on that – that increases their knowledge, experience and skills, lets them be involved in different groups and contribute, makes them feel valued as well. For example, one guy who is a support worker who has good values, etc went on a person centred planning facilitator's course, really impressed them, got on really well – he came along to our regional network – and got really fired up about his course on graphic facilitation. So we got him to speak on that – the pros and cons and all the rest of it. I wanted to get him to do the minutes for the regional network and use his skills and abilities to produce the minutes in accessible formats. So he is going to be able to put that into practice, going to be our consultant on that kind of thing.'

In this chapter I focus on the relevance of personal (and professional) development planning to managers and senior practitioners. In particular I deal with:

- the meaning of personal and professional development planning
- why personal and professional development is important to managers
- the personal and professional development planning process
- self-appraisal: identifying and prioritising personal development needs
- deciding on development goals
- personal strengths and limitations in relation to personal health and well-being and your job role
- the challenges of personal and professional development to managers and senior practitioners

The meaning of personal and professional development planning

Personal (and professional) development planning (PDP) means identifying your own learning and development needs, devising an action plan to meet these needs, keeping track of how the action plan is going and reviewing it regularly to make the necessary changes. This process is usually represented cyclically. For example:

Self-appraisal
(identifying your development needs)

Action planning
(setting development goals and identifying ways of achieving them)

Reviewing your plan

**Implementing and monitoring
your action plan**

PDP and you

PDP should be a continuous process, linked to day-to-day practice and an integral aspect of your development as a manager or senior practitioner. You should have charge of the process and your own plan, with support and guidance from a facilitator, usually your line manager. Your organisation may or may not have a framework for undertaking PDP. The first step in PDP is to identify your development needs and interests and express these in terms of development goals. After this, it's usual to meet with a facilitator (often the line manager, but maybe another senior colleague) to discuss and agree the development goals and devise a plan for achieving these goals. The facilitator also has an important role in supporting the implementation of the plan, monitoring progress and in the review and further development of the plan, the latter usually done on an annual basis, although some organisations have more frequent reviews. The facilitator should also be accessible at other times for discussion and support – easier if he or she is also your supervisor.

The role of the facilitator

During the initial planning process, the facilitator has a responsibility to:

- ensure confidentiality, equality and non-discrimination

- be sensitive to your needs

- be well prepared for the planning process and clear about the requirements and procedures of the organisation with regard to PDP, as well as the PDP process

- encourage free and honest discussion

- adopt a positive focus which recognises your strengths and talents while promoting critical self-appraisal

Your role in these meetings

Your role in these meetings is to:

- prepare well for the process

- express your development needs and intended goals as fully as possible, discussing and negotiating as necessary

- be honest and self-critical

- be prepared to acknowledge your own strengths as well as your development needs, something that professionals do not always find easy

Both of you have a responsibility to agree your development goals and to document these in whatever way is decided within the organisation or, if this is flexible, in a way that suits you both.

Thereafter, you have a responsibility to yourself and your organisation to ensure that you implement your plan as well as you can and monitor your own learning and development progress. Since this is something you do anyway as part of your work, eg by applying to attend training events and reporting back on these through regular supervision with your line manager or other senior colleague this should be relatively easy to do, possibly with some adjustments to your way of working.

The facilitator has a responsibility to support your learning and development, assist in obtaining the necessary resources, support your requests for training where this has been agreed in your development plan, support you in overcoming any obstacles and be available to help with the monitoring of your plan and for the review process.

Here's what one manager said about development planning in her organisation:

'Through our training and development plan we have a document which is a personal action plan. So after you have been on the course or had the experience you fill that in and this helps you reflect: What have I learned from that? What do I need to do now? What have I learned from this course or this coaching? How am I going to make a difference when I go back into practice? So we do that. Sometimes when there are critical incidents we use that – whatever the critical incident might be (it might be a complaint, an error, or it might have been an accident, something that couldn't be anticipated) then as a group we look at that: How can we do that differently? What have we learned from that? How could we prevent that in the future? So we use that kind of thing as well. We use that at all levels in training, at manager and organisational level too.'

PDP is not the same as performance appraisal, but may be incorporated into it. If PDP is part of appraisal it is important to ensure that the individual employee remains in control of his or her own PDP process and that development needs and aspirations are compatible with, and not sublimated to, those of the organisation. At the same time, the employee's responsibility to the organisation has to be recognised.

PDP is closely related to continuing professional development (CPD) but is usually more comprehensive and sometimes more flexible. We can think of CPD as being the aspects of personal and development planning that equates to the learning events and activities we engage in to realise our development goals. Some professional bodies have specific requirements with regard to CPD. Professional development has always been important to organisations since it is the quality of staff that determines the quality of the service. But it is the emphasis on the *personal* component which marks PDP out as innovative. Both *personal* and *professional* aspects of development are equally important. In PDP, development is seen primarily as the responsibility of the individual, although with the full support of the organisation. This is a departure from more traditional views of professionalism where objectivity, distance and emotional detachment were stressed (though in reality neither truly possible nor practised in entirety). Currently, we tend towards a more holistic and integrated understanding of professionalism which acknowledges the relationship between the personal and the professional aspects of practice and the impact of one upon the other. Distinction is often made between the 'technical' aspects of the job role, acquired through training, and those which result from personal experience and informal on-the-job learning.

The way in which organisations approach Personal and Professional Development Planning is influenced considerably by their understanding of what constitutes professional development. Clegg, Tan and Saeiddi (2002) argue the need to 'widen our conceptualisation of professional development and the relationship between its active and reflective components' (p. 143), as well as to recognise the range of ways in which people approach their own professional development.

Why personal and professional development is important to managers

There is a close link between the development of individual employees and the quality of the service provided by an organisation. NHS Scotland describes personal development planning and review as 'part of a continual process of planning, monitoring, assessment and support to help staff develop their capabilities and potential to fulfil their job role and purpose. It is an approach to increase the effectiveness of the organisation's performance through ongoing, constructive dialogue to ensure that everyone:

- knows what is expected of them

- gets feedback on performance

- is able to identify and satisfy their development needs' (p. 6)

(www.show.scot.nhs.uk/spf/PIN%20Consultation%20Docs/PersonalDevelopt.PDF)

In practice, they advocate that such planning should take place at least on an annual basis, focus on self-assessment with the support of a facilitator and be given the time necessary to make the process effective.

Northumbria University (http://online.northumbria.ac.uk) compares a Personal Development Plan (PDP) to a roadmap which keeps a person focused on specific objectives, identifies achievable goals and allows progress to be measured.

The Scottish Qualifications Authority defines PDP as:

> 'a process that enables individuals to identify, manage and develop their skills, experience and learning. It is a dynamic process that helps individuals clarify and achieve personal, education and career aims. In completing the process it demonstrates to others, such as employers, academic selectors or admissions tutors, that the individual is able to think critically about their own development and take appropriate action to achieve goals' (www.sqa.org.uk/files_ccc/Tutor_Guide_PDP.pdf).

Example of good practice

The Central Scotland Office of Community Integrated Care (CIC), a company which provides services for people with learning disabilities, older people and people with mental health needs, achieved their *Investors in People Scotland* recognition in 2003. Here is an extract from the feedback report:

'CIC has a Management Development Programme to ensure that all managers within the organisation have the skills and knowledge to carry out their people management responsibilities. Gaps in skills are identified using a Management Skills Profile checklist. Managers at all levels throughout the company described how they had been encouraged to develop their management skills through individual training courses under the Management Development Programme, coaching from other managers and attendance at the quarterly Development Days, as well as taking part in Appraisal Training. People who had been promoted to management positions described how they had attended a week long New Managers Induction course.'

Most managers, like the ones I spoke to, believe that their own personal and professional development is reflected in the quality of the service.

'Something that I had to think about recently, in terms of being really frustrated in my job – I'm not feeling that I don't have a lot to continue to give, it just needs to be different for me in some ways because the kind of fire-fighting same stuff day in and day out just doesn't help me feel that I am achieving very much. So a bit of the focus that I have been doing is looking at the development in terms of small teams. And so their development will help my development, because one of the areas that I feel I kind of need to develop in is around, sure, that you move things forward in a proactive rather than reactive way – because you do; it is reactive, day in and day out, but that doesn't actually give anybody a sense of movement, I don't think. Fine, people move, but they just don't see that they do. And I certainly found that I've found it hard to see where it was going. So in terms of developing the service I've tried to structure that into me taking more of a proactive role and hopefully that will help me feel that I am actually doing something.'

'I think personal development for me is very much dependent on your own level of self-awareness, and I think that is very much about the kind of person you are, the experiences you've had in life and how they helped you develop. And I think if you are aware then you might be more aware of the need to develop and that might make it easier for you to go and ask. But I know a big part of my role as a supervisor is helping workers to think about their needs to develop and how do we facilitate that, can we do that, can it be done through supervision? There might be something – there might be skills with which I can help them, or do they need to go to some other professional person? We might be able to access some very cheap training opportunities. But I don't kind of get that from my supervision, and I think a part of that is because you are so focused on the bigger picture. If you don't ask for it, if you don't say, well, I feel I need to develop in this way, or I feel that I'm stagnating doing this and I need to be challenged more. I don't feel the opportunities are there, the professional development structure – there aren't a lot of opportunities to link into that.'

Taking charge of your own learning and development

As is clear from the foregoing discussion, one of the principles of PDP is that the individual employee is in control of the process, although within organisational requirements and guidelines. It is right that we *should* be in control of our own personal and professional development, but sometimes other things can get in the way, such as organisational systems or staff or resource shortages. In the activity on the next page, I've listed some of the reasons why I think it is important to ensure that we keep charge of our own job-related development. Rate these in order of importance from your own perspective.

ACTIVITY 5: **Controlling our own personal and professional development**

In your opinion, how important is each of these reasons relative to another? Rate them by writing '1' beside the most important, '2' beside the next most important and so on.

It's important for me to identify my personal learning needs because:

☐ It helps me gain a deeper insight into my own practice.

☐ I have a responsibility for my own personal and professional development.

☐ Knowing myself better means I can support and manage other staff more effectively.

☐ I owe it to myself.

☐ I owe it to the organisation.

☐ It's part of my job.

☐ It puts me more in control of my own practice.

☐ It gives me a better idea of how to meet my own learning needs.

☐ I owe it to service users.

☐ I'm committed to lifelong learning.

☐ It makes it easier to get support from the organisation.

☐ It helps me understand more about my own learning and development.

You might also want to add other reasons which you consider more important than those I've listed.

Comment

I wonder whether you found any conflicts in rating the different items. It may be that your reasons are considerably different from mine. Whatever you said, I'm sure you agree that it's your right to be in control of your own learning and development and that you're by far the best person to be so. You may also have thought that you seldom have the time to do this properly in a busy job – which is probably one of the reasons you're reading this book, and/or doing a LDAF qualification. Sometimes it's important to take time out from your regular work to consider and plan your own development. Your organisation should be taking your professional development seriously and providing time and support for all staff to engage in an ongoing process of personal and professional development planning.

Personal and professional development planning is important because it:

- focuses upon each of us as individuals, with our own strengths and talents

- puts us in charge of our own personal and professional development

- highlights the organisation's responsibility towards all employees, but also their responsibility to the organisation and the people they support

- enables us to take account of all learning and not just that leading to formal qualifications

- opens doors to more innovative forms of learning and development

- enables us to track our own progress and development and provide evidence of both

The personal and professional development planning process

PDP involves a considerable amount of reflection: where am I now, what have I learned, where do I want to get to in the future and what's the best way of getting there? The process is the one identified in the diagram on page 39. Have a look back at the diagram to remind yourself of the four stages in the cycle, then use the information which follows to work through the four stages.

Self-appraisal (identifying your development needs)

This involves reflection on a number of job related issues:

- how you perceive your job

- the organisational context of your work

- the requirements of your job, ie your roles and responsibilities and how well you fulfil them; the values, attitudes, skills, knowledge, capacities and personal qualities you bring to your job

- what else you need to learn, eg gaps in your knowledge, skills and capacities you need for your role as it is now and as it is likely to develop in the future

The next four activities will help you think about these aspects of your job and lead you to identify your development goals.

ACTIVITY 6: **How you perceive your job**

Begin by listing three of the main responsibilities of your job.

Next, describe how you feel about your job, in one sentence.

List three things you most enjoy about your job.

List three things you find most challenging about your job and that you feel least well equipped for.

Where do you get most support for fulfilling your job role?

What else could the organisation do to support your ongoing learning and development?

Comment

You will be aware that I was asking you to use a considerable amount of reflection in this activity. You'll almost certainly have thought about or talked about the issues I raised, possibly on many occasions. Has putting them down on paper like this helped you to clarify any of them or is it something you have done before?

It would be unrealistic and unprofessional to think about personal development needs in isolation. We all have a responsibility to the organisation which employs us, the primary one of which is to pursue the goals and objectives of the organisation, as long as these are not in conflict with the rights of the people being supported. Assuming that everyone in your organisation shares the same vision and goals, ie the social inclusion of people with learning disabilities and the upholding of their rights as full and participating citizens, your development goals should reflect those of the organisation as a whole. In the next activity you are asked to think about this.

ACTIVITY 7: **The organisational context of your job**

What do you most like about the organisation you work for and why?

What do you least like and why?

Where does most of your support come from in the organisation?

What is the main aim of your organisation?

What is your organisation best at?

What is your organisation least good at?

Describe how your organisation promotes social inclusion for service users.

How do you help to further the aims and fulfil your role in your organisation?

Have a look at your job description. To what extent does it reflect what you do in practice at the current time? Does it need updating – if so, how?

Are your priorities and those of your organisation in accord with one another? If not, what are the problems?

How might you resolve these problems and who could help?

Comment

Given that every service is striving to improve its performance, your ability to identify shortcomings not only in your own work, but in the performance of the service, is crucial to optimal development and the realisation of the vision. This activity was designed to help you think about your feelings about your organisation and the extent to which you feel comfortable and supported within it. Support is crucial if you are to do a good job. If you identified any problems, can you discuss these with someone you trust and work towards a resolution?

The next stage in the PDP process is to think about your own skills and capacities and how these match your job role. Activity 8 should help you explore this. In it I have listed some of the competencies managers and senior practitioners require. These are based upon the LDAF units of the Higher Professional Diploma. Rate the items for your own practice, with 5 meaning 'I am very good at this' and 1 being 'I need to improve in this'. Be as honest as you can – this is your own personal self-appraisal.

ACTIVITY 8: **Your roles and responsibilities**

This activity is in two parts.

Part 1: Personal and professional competencies
Rate each of the following items on a scale of 1 (need to improve) to
5 (I am very good) which you feel applies to your own capacity.

☐ Having a well-informed knowledge of current issues in services for people with learning disabilities

☐ Approaching all aspects of my work in a person centred way

☐ Reflecting effectively on my own practice and learning from insights

☐ Ensuring protection for service users from abuse, neglect and exploitation

☐ Promoting and supporting empowerment of service users and carers

☐ Promoting equality, diversity and rights

☐ Making effective use of performance management systems for myself and staff I manage and/or supervise

☐ Adapting my communication to the needs of different individuals and groups, eg service users, carers, other professionals, etc

☐ Promoting and supporting social inclusion and citizenship

☐ Using local, regional and national networks effectively

☐ Co-ordinating, monitoring and reviewing service quality

☐ Specialist knowledge in relation to services users you work with, eg therapeutic approaches, alternative and augmentative communication, support with continence or other health areas, citizen and self-advocacy, etc

☐ Knowledge and skill in other significant aspects of work, eg challenging behaviour, relationships and sexuality, mental health, etc

☐ Managing and effecting change

☐ Staff leadership and management

☐ Managing financial resources

☐ ICT skills

☐ Joint working with other agencies

☐ Staff recruitment and selection

☐ Managing volunteers

☐ Deputising for more senior colleagues

Part 2: Perceptions of you as a manager or senior practitioner

Next, think about how you perceive yourself as a manager or senior practitioner and how other people see you.

How would you describe yourself as a manager/senior practitioner?

How would your colleagues describe you? (You might like to ask them)

How would your line manager describe you? (You might like to ask him or her)

How would people using your service describe you? (You might like to ask them)

Are there any differences in the various perspectives? If so, what accounts for them?

Taken together, do these impressions give a fair account of you as a professional? If not, what's missing and/or inaccurate and why?

Comment

Being a manager or senior practitioner in a service for people with learning disabilities is a complex commitment which is impossible to sum up in a short space. It's also an ongoing process of development. Have a look at the areas where you rated yourself highly in part 1. Are your skills and talents being used to full effect in your current post? If not, how could they be better used? Now have a look at the areas where you rated yourself lowest. These will help you start to identify gaps in your own capacities, ie your development needs.

In part 2, if there were discrepancies in different people's perceptions, including your own, are you comfortable with these? If not, what concerns you and does this help you to identify any development needs?

Another method often used to enable people to explore their own development needs is SWOT (Strengths, Weaknesses, Opportunities and Threats) analysis. If you haven't yet undertaken a SWOT analysis for your own job, you might like to have a go at it now by doing the next activity.

ACTIVITY 9: **SWOT analysis**

Strengths
List the things you are particularly good at and which help you do a good job. Remember to think about other people's appraisal of you as well as your own.

Weaknesses
List the weaknesses which get in the way of doing a good job, eg what aren't you good at; what should you avoid?

Opportunities
List all the things you can think of that present you with opportunities for personal development, eg training, changes in direction of the service, new legislation, local networks, supportive colleagues, etc

Threats
List the barriers and obstacles you face; these might come from within yourself, eg lack of confidence, not keeping up to date, too heavy a workload; from the organisation, eg lack of direction or leadership, shortage of resources, outmoded ways of working; or from other external sources, eg policy changes (which can be both opportunities and threats at the same time); underfunding.

Comment

How did you get on? Having identified these different items, you can now use the information to plan how you can make best use of your strengths and opportunities, overcome weaknesses and deal with threats. In other words, to devise a development plan based on your SWOT analysis.

You might like to...

...look at some websites which discuss SWOT analysis. For example:

http://www.scotland.gov.uk/Topics/Government/FOI/18593/13940

http://www.wiley.co.uk/wileychi/innovate/website/pages/atoz/swot.htm

SWOT analysis highlights the importance of acknowledging your own strengths as well as your limitations. The job of manager or senior practitioner in an organisation supporting people with learning disabilities and their families is a demanding one. Rarely do you get much time to think about yourself, which is why you need to *make* time.

Action planning (setting development goals and identifying ways of achieving them)

The action planning process involves:

- setting your development goals

- meeting with your facilitator to commit your action plan to paper (or computer) and to identify appropriate methods of achieving your goals

- agreeing your action plan between the two of you, with goals, methods, timescales, resources and support agreed and specified

Activity 10 is about setting your own development goals.

ACTIVITY 10: **Setting development goals**

Look back at Activity 8 and choose two areas you scored low. Imagine you were writing a PDP to help you improve on these areas. Express each item as a development goal.

Comment

I can't know which areas you chose to concentrate on, but I've taken two examples just to show how the process might work: 'managing financial resources' and 'deputising for more senior colleagues' and imagined a score of 2 for each. I then expressed the goals as follows:

Managing financial resources:

- to develop the skills and knowledge for budgetary management and accounting in relation to the resources I have charge of

- to familiarise myself with the organisation's new system for budgetary management and use this in managing my own budget

Deputising for more senior colleagues:

- to learn more about management styles, reflect on my own strengths and weaknesses so that I can work to strengths and identify ways of overcoming my weaknesses

- to seek peer and management perspectives on my strengths and weaknesses in managing people

(These goals can be refined further as the planning process develops.)

You now need to meet with your facilitator, agree the goals and draw up a plan of action with which you both agree. This should include:

- methods of achieving your goals (your learning strategies)

- the timescale

- the required resources and support needed

- a date for reviewing your progress and the effectiveness of the plan (usually done annually but sometimes more frequently)

These steps enable you to move through the remaining stages of the process:

- implementing and monitoring your action plan

- reviewing your plan

Your organisation may have a prescribed method of doing all this, or may leave it up to each individual and facilitator to devise a system which suits, usually in accordance with organisational guidelines. You may also have looked at other structures and formats on the internet.

As you would expect, there are many different ways of approaching PDP, from very simple to incredibly complex. As Trumper (2004) tells us, Personal Development Plans are both personal and unique – there are no hard and fast rules about what they look like or about what goes into them. Tamkin et al (1995) explain:
'A Personal Development Plan can vary considerably in focus. A plan may concentrate purely on development needed to perform better.'

Another approach used in PDP is *gap analysis*, which I want to look at briefly as you may find it helpful in your own planning.

Gap analysis

Gap analysis can be used to provide people with the opportunity to compare their current capacities with those required in the job role and then 'fill in the gaps' through a variety of learning events and activities. The process is:

- define the present state of affairs

- define the desired or target state

- identify ways of filling the gap between the present and target state, eg ask what has to happen to achieve the desired or target state

Imagine, for example, that you are unable to use a computer, but that your job requires you to do so increasingly for e-mails, record keeping, event sharing and so on. Your desired state is to be able to do all the computer tasks required of you, so you could list these tasks quite easily, possibly with help from someone who knows computer literacy well. Then you could prioritise the tasks. It would make sense to start with the easiest and work towards the most complex. You need to identify the resources and opportunities needed and draw up your plan of action, with a timeline, embark on your plan, monitor its effectiveness and evaluate your progress at specific intervals. But you also need to ensure that you can maintain the desired state of affairs once you have arrived there, so this might mean continuing support, for example. It will also mean practice, since it's not enough to be able to do the thing adequately if it takes you forever to complete one form – you need to overlearn the skills in order to be as efficient as possible. Defining the target with performance criteria helps ensure efficiency.

It's fairly easy to apply gap analysis for technical skills such as computer literacy but much more difficult to use the approach in more complex areas, such as supporting people in relationships or promoting equality and diversity, for example.

When identifying the gaps in your own capacities, you have to take account not only of what is required of you now, but also how the job is likely to change in the future. For example, staff in supported living services find that they are more likely than they once were to be supporting people with profound and multiple learning disabilities because of hospital closures. The basic knowledge and skills they require to do this are essentially the same as those required to support any individual, but there are also differences, especially in relation to communication, moving and handling and health care, for example. Some future needs are unknown, of course, but we can usually make well informed guesses about others.

ACTIVITY 11: **Filling the gap**

This activity is a continuation of the previous one. Look back at Activity 8 again. Choose another area on which you rated yourself low on the scale. Describe the present and target states.

Now list a number of manageable steps required to reach the target state and put these steps in order of priority according to the requirements of your job.

Next, identify the support and resources you require to help you work through these steps and reach the target state.

Comment

What you have done here is to draw up an action plan in this area of your work. The next step will be to combine this information into a format such as the one below and to decide on timescale and performance criteria or evidence. You can follow a similar procedure for other aspects of your job role.

The 'desired state' defines your development goals, which can be sub-divided into *measurable* objectives. This means that the language used to express the objectives is crucial. For example, it is easier to assess progress against an objective expressed thus: 'To attend a Makaton course and reach the required standard for level 1' than one that says 'To improve my communication with people who don't speak'.

Whatever methods you use for development planning, one of the challenges is to decide how simple or complex to make your analysis. It would be perfectly possible to spend all your time analysing your own capacities but never doing anything about them – or doing this instead of working! Once your development needs have been identified you also need to prioritise them. Common sense dictates that development planning must be reasonable, realistic and manageable. You also need to ensure that your development priorities are compatible with those of your organisation.

Challenges for managers and senior practitioners in relation to personal and professional development planning and review

In Activities 8 and 9, you identified some of your own shortcomings, things that might get in the way of doing the kind of job you feel you should be doing. These will form some of the challenges you face in PDP. But some of the challenges will come from other sources – workplace culture, workload and changing demands in services, for example. There's certainly no shortage! Managers I spoke to told me about some of the challenges they have to meet.

'I think that's been an area [personal and professional development] that probably has frustrated me for a long time, and I've been a manager for 13 years. And, up until I got the opportunity to do the SVQ4, there had been a number of years prior to that where there really hadn't been anything on offer. And I think that's because – a lot of that, I think, is because of the sheer number of workers that have come into the services, and the focus on getting people a value base and a depth of knowledge to support the complexities – it was a bit of a frustration, because my worry is that you would stagnate in terms of the job. You wouldn't stagnate on a daily basis, because the demands are so many and so varied, but it's quite often fire-fighting, isn't it? It's like crisis management – sometimes that feels like 100 per cent of the job, but it's probably always about 80 per cent plus of the job anyway – and I think that doesn't sustain you, in terms of the sense of your own direction, and SVQ4 presented that opportunity for me to kind of consolidate it. But I'm through that process now and I don't know, in terms of the organisation, what there is there. And I suppose that would be my focus.'

'Slightly different experience for me. I haven't been in post as long as X – I've only been in post as a manager for five years. I had the manager's foundation course to do, which is a useful in-house course because it allows you to look at different areas and gives you an awareness of, perhaps, what information you need to be a manager, what skills you need, what decisions you might take and what are the pitfalls of those. There was a couple of years' gap then you had SVQ, following on to the back of that, so then again SVQ was useful development as well. But as X says, then you get out the other side of that. I think you do need something; you need something else there because you go to your work and, although the difficulties are different on a daily basis, it's the same kind of work that you are doing. You could describe it as repetitive, in that what you do is that you go, and there will be issues that surround people's lives that you deal with on a daily basis. And that's just an ongoing and very fluid problem that you have to deal with. But having something new to go off and do is also what I think you're looking for at times.'

'But sometimes it's about focusing on something. I enjoy being challenged and having my views challenged, and that doesn't actually happen a great deal as a manager. Workers might challenge you but they challenge you very much coming from their place and normally you've got an argument because you've gone through the process and you've been a part of the risk assessment and everything on whatever situation, so it isn't challenging. Individual supervision – in terms of my own management – tends to be looking at service issues; it doesn't necessarily look at what I need to develop. And I think that's sometimes the greatest challenge when we come together with our managers – and we do that – but we have very limited opportunities for it.'

'It [day-to-day work supporting staff] doesn't provide you with the positive side of challenge, like SVQ4 does. Having that SVQ4 was a challenge, was a positive experience – as an individual you had to develop within yourself to gain knowledge – you had the opportunity. One of the kind of most positive things about SVQ4 was that we met one day per month as a group in order to look at the work that was being done, look at the work we had to do ahead and to go over that work and to think about, you know, where would you find that in your work, have you encountered that before, what did you do, had you not encountered it before, what would you do in that situation, what options are around it.'

Nowadays we're much more aware of things like stress, bullying and 'burn-out' in the workplace, but we're still not taking it as seriously as we should. Saunders (*Guardian*, 10 January 2005), writing about the 'wall of silence surrounding stress', said that although five million people think their jobs are stressful and half a million say workplace stress is making them ill, they will not speak up about this at work because they are afraid of being considered weak, inefficient and a failure.

Radical changes in an organisation bring particular stress, as these managers testified. But they also recognised in such circumstances the opportunity for in-depth reflection and professional and personal development.

'It certainly pushed my coping strategies to the limit, and I think a lot of that was that the changes were all happening and there were so many local changes as well and that, coupled with some really complex support issues, it kind of burned me out, to an extent. But I think part of it was I hadn't changed the way I looked at it – it's always been a really challenging job, it's always been a big service. I suppose a lot of the painful learning that I had to do was, well, I can't change a lot of this, I can change me, and I think the pressure of doing SVQ alongside everything – because I was really up for the changes; it was something that I had believed in for a lot longer than it was ever going to happen – but I still think I was unprepared for the increase of demand on us. And what actually happened was that more responsibility got put on at a time when probably less support was there. And so you were kind of left feeling isolated a bit because the people who were able to give you more support three years ago are less available now. And because – I think just because of the sheer demand – I remember the CU7 [part of the training] that reflects on around your own development and finding that really easy to do because it was so fresh, and you knew how you learned, and maybe that was the first opportunity for a long time for me, to actually stop and say, well, what is my learning style? What does influence me? What motivates me to change? And I don't think we thought about that to that point – you don't do you? You just do it.'

'I think the other side of that as well is the fact that there were timescales involved and there was a very definite place to go to. You had a rough idea of where you wanted to go and you had to find a path in order to get there. And that was beneficial in many ways. You know, if you take away the other stuff about pressures that were placed on you to have a timescale and to complete your SVQ at the same time – the timescale in itself wasn't entirely a negative thing because you knew that you kind of had to get to that point – I think when you take that away, because there have been days after that period where I have certainly had this conversation a number of times with my line manager, that I feel that we are stuck at some point where we have moved a very sizeable chunk in terms of how we've changed the service and have still development of the service to do, but there's no timescale on that, no immediacy to do it. You know there's nothing that's forcing you to do it. One of the things that will happen for ourselves in the next financial year, which again will create the right kind of climate for change, I think, is that we'll redevelop part of the service within the fiscal year, so it has to be done within a timescale. It's an enormous piece of work, because it will take 26 weeks for the development to be done. We'll be decanting people, they'll get used to new support structures, and there'll be all of those huge pieces of work all hanging together. But that's all right because we know at the end of the day we'll be coming back to support people to live in houses of their own within the inside of this building and there will be timescales that provide pressure for us and motivation. And also, all of the things that will be there in order to motivate you into working a certain agenda will be more apparent than they are at the moment, because we do know that we have to continue to develop the service, and be seen to develop the service, and we do try to continue to develop the service, particularly in terms of lifestyle plans.'

They described their own ways of managing the stress and the demands of the job.

'I learned that as well – and maybe it's the nature of management to an extent as well – that you do have a lot of demands on you. You sometimes wonder if the perception is very different from the reality although at times the demands are less. But I think sometimes you feel – I know myself – sometimes you feel overwhelmed by what you have to get through. But when I sit down and I structure it and I set timescales on it, it takes the overwhelming feeling out of it. And I remember having a conversation with my assessor who said, "Put a timescale on it; you'll not do it otherwise, because you do it when there's timescales". And I thought that, as one of the bits of learning I did, if you tell me to have it done by next Wednesday, I'll do it because I am too stubborn to not do it. And a big bit of that is about my personality. But if you tell me just to get it into you in a couple of months it'll lie there until the day before you ask for it, and then I'll do it. I don't know if a bit of that is just there are so many demands that sometimes you maybe need some structure and some constraints built in.'

'I have become more effective. I am much clearer on the boundaries and I also think that I learned a lot about the role of managers, having gone through a period of intense stress. That made me have to kind of re-evaluate what the manager's role is for me. It doesn't stop me getting frustrated at times – all of those are occupational hazards – but it did help me understand the bits that I could change, and made me think around that. So I don't think it was a wasted experience in any way, for all it was difficult. I think that sometimes as the manager you have to put your ego aside a bit. Because other people expect so much of you doesn't mean to say you have as much to give. And I think there's been a bit of that – just sometimes thinking, consciously or otherwise, around why you are doing what you are doing. That helps you work within a context that's maybe a bit clearer. I think frequently we talk about things running away from us – I think that's how it feels, but I think it feels that way for me because I don't actually think about where I am in it.'

If stress is an issue for *you*, you need to do something about it – and the sooner the better.

Challenges in PDP can come from:

- unrealistic expectations of yourself – Are you a 'perfectionist', setting yourself up to fail because perfection is an impossibility? It's much better to be an 'as-good-as–I-can-be-in–the-situation' type of person.

- overwork – Assess whose fault this is (your own or someone else's?). Are you getting enough support? Are you taking on someone else's workload? Are you unable to say no?

- not taking days off and holidays – Are you guilty of this and if so, why?

- role confusion – Are you clear about your own responsibilities? If not, clarify them.

- not being in charge of your own development planning – Find out the organisation's policy on this and if it is being followed. If it's 'top-down' who can support you in getting it changed?

- other people's management style – Is this relevant to you and how can you deal with it? What personal strengths and colleague support do you have?

- a poor work–life balance – How well balanced is yours?

- being undervalued and not having your skills and knowledge well used – It's important to be aware of your own skills and worth to the organisation and to discuss these in your PDP.

- not getting appropriate training – Do you know where to find out about training and what your entitlement is in the job?

- a poor physical environment which can affect your health (over-crowding, lots of noise, insufficient or too much heat or light, lack of opportunity for moving about and so on) – Just being aware of this can make you do something about it. Health and safety guidance will help.

There are many other things that can get in the way of your PDP and you can probably add to my list. The important thing is to act – either on your own, but more likely, with colleagues, if you are affected by any of these factors.

You might like to...

...log on to the following website which provides guidance on work related stress, bullying and harassment and mental health:

Mental Health Foundation www.mentalhealth.org.uk

...read *Tackling the effects of stress* by Dr Penny Gray
Details on http:// www.mentalhealth.org.uk/page.cfm?pagecode=PBBFMW

However, the limitations and constraints that impede PDP must not cause you to lose sight of your own strengths. Capitalising on your strengths and talents will make your job much more satisfying and this will have a profound effect on the quality of your practice. Look back at Activities 6, 8 and 9 to remind yourself of your strengths. Are you making the most of these and do you appreciate your own value to your organisation. If not, what are you going to do about this?

PDP and your work with people with learning disabilities

PDP is particularly important in people-orientated services like the one in which you work. People who are disempowered experience social oppression and are often vulnerable and need professionals who will uphold their rights and safeguard their interests. The better you know yourself, the more equipped you will be to do this. This is particularly crucial for managers and senior practitioners who lead other staff by example and through supervision. The effect of organisational culture on employees has been well researched and it is the leaders who set the tone.

Involving service users in your PDP process

In Activity 8 I suggested that you might explore how service users perceive you. Even if you didn't do this, you will have a good idea from people's comments and the way they relate to you of how they see you. Your PDP process will be all the richer for involving service users in whatever way you deem appropriate and feel comfortable with. If people communicate verbally you might, for example, invite them to 'think with you' about things you are particularly good at, or not so good at. You might build into activities opportunities for assessing the quality of support you provide for people. Recruitment and interviewing are also useful times for enabling people with learning disabilities to provide you with feedback.

Examples

In its training activities, the Scottish Consortium for Learning Disability (SCLD) includes people with learning disabilities as co-trainers with professionals and family carers. Following the training event there is opportunity for the co-trainer with a learning disability to provide feedback to the professional on the type and level of support provided, which enables the person concerned to reflect on and improve his or her performance.

The British Institute of Learning Disabilities (BILD), like several other organisations, includes people with learning disabilities on interview panels. There are opportunities for the person or people involved to advise the others on the panel about the kind of support they prefer. Following the interviews, debriefing enables reflection on what worked well and what didn't and can provide insight for the non-disabled panel members.

ACTIVITY 12: **Involving service users in your PDP**

Describe two or three ways in which you could realistically involve service users (or their relatives if the people concerned require advocacy support) in your PDP.

Comment

I can't know what you've suggested as it will be personal to your own situation, but I hope the activity gave you an opportunity to think about the extent to which service users already inform your PDP, eg through feedback they provide when involved in policy-making, activity and event planning, training and staff selection, as well as other ways in which they could support your PDP.

Concluding comments

Personal and professional development planning should be a powerful and rewarding experience for you, enabling you not only to be in charge of your own development, but also to make demands on the organisation which employs you, get the best out of opportunities available and provide the highest quality of service for people with learning disabilities and their families.

PDP can increase job satisfaction, decrease frustration, help you to use your skills and talents more effectively and improve the quality of service provided by your organisation, now and in the future. Having invested time and effort in devising and agreeing your development plan, the next stage is to put it into practice, keeping track of your progress. You should have access to a wide range of options which can help you achieve these goals. However, reality dictates that the learning opportunities you use must be feasible in relation to your workload, the requirements of your organisation and the personal and professional development needs and plans of colleagues. In chapter 3 I explore a variety of learning opportunities you might pursue, considering their appropriateness for your development goals, your own approach to learning and the organisational context.

Chapter 3

Learning and professional development

Introduction

A well-structured development plan may look good on paper, or computer, but the test comes when it is put into effect. That's when you can see whether your development goals square with the reality of your day-to-day practice and are achievable. It's when the question of learning comes into play. In particular, what kind of learning can best help us achieve our development goals and how can we evaluate what we have learned?

As adult learners we learn best when our learning is self directed, ie when we are in control and learning is relevant and manageable. We can improve our capacity for learning by planning well, analysing our own approach to learning and being clear about the principles of effective learning. These are the issues I discuss in this chapter, with reference to:

- what constitutes learning

- what suits you best in learning

- the learning cycle and learning styles

- monitoring and reviewing learning and associated development

What do we meaning by 'learning'?

Learning can be simple or complex, planned or incidental, immediate or long term. In fact, anything that results in a change in understanding or behaviour is recognised as learning. Take incidental learning, for example. Often, we don't even notice we're learning and it's only when we reflect on the experience that we realise that learning has taken place. This is how we master many things that then become automatic, such as the 'mechanics' of everyday routines and the niceties of casual acquaintance. I say 'Good morning' to you, you smile and reply. I don't bother saying good morning to Arthur because he's always miserable and doesn't bother answering. I've learned to adapt my morning 'greeting' behaviour to two different situations. At home, if I'm making one cup of coffee I put very little water in the kettle because I don't want to waste water or electricity. If I'm making four I'll fill the kettle to the maximum. I've learned through experience that this is how to do it.

Some learning involves straightforward memorisation and retrieval of information – remembering your pin number, for example. But this is only useful if you also learn how to use the cashpoint or the chip and pin machine (not so long ago this was a mystery to many of us – now it's commonplace). It's not only the *what* that matters in learning, but the *how to*.

Lots of people have been, and still are, very interested in what learning is all about, so theories abound and thinking changes. Smith (2003) writes: 'Pick up a standard psychology textbook – especially from the 1960s and 1970s – and you will probably find learning defined as a change in behaviour. In other words, learning is approached as an outcome – the end product of some process. It can be recognised or seen. This approach has the virtue of highlighting a crucial aspect of learning – change' (reproduced from the *encyclopaedia of informal education*, www.infed.org). However, as Smith points out, that's only one aspect of learning. In reality it's much more complex and both process and outcome are important.

According to Skinner and others the idea of learning as an outcome owes much to behaviourism, whereas Maslow and Rogers adopted a humanistic stance, Piaget, Gagne and Bruner a cognitive approach, Kolb an experiential orientation and other theorists a variety of other perspectives (Smith, 2003). To a large extent it all depends on your starting point and all of these theories have helped us understand the principles of effective learning.

Saljo (1979) asked a number of adult students what they understood by learning and categorised their responses thus:

- a quantitative increase in knowledge – acquiring information or 'knowing a lot'

- memorising – storing information that can be reproduced

- acquiring facts, skills and methods that can be retained and used as necessary

- making sense of abstract meaning – relating parts of the subject matter to each other and to the real world

- interpreting and understanding reality in a different way – comprehending the world by reinterpreting knowledge

Research into adult learning shows that:

- Adults have expectations about the learning process and bring their own uniqueness to learning in terms of experiences and values.

- Learning is assimilated with previous life experience.

- Learning needs to be active and relevant to life.

Thus, as adults, we learn best when:

- We are in control of our own learning and have choice in deciding what to learn.

- We are actively involved in all stages of the learning process – planning, designing, doing, reflecting on and evaluating the effect.

- Our individual needs and strengths are taken into account.

- New learning builds on our past experience and on our interests.

- The context is conducive to learning, eg free of competing demands, provides necessary support and resources, work culture encourages learning, values people – and so on.

- We can see the sense in, and value of, what we are learning and can apply it to life.

Malcolm Knowles (1990), well known for his research into, and theories of, adult learning, believed that the most appropriate form of learning for adults is self-directed learning, something we've come to accept. Support for adult learning is generally more productive if it is facilitative rather than didactic. Knowles drew upon the theories of Lewin, Schon and Piaget. His work has influenced that of many other researchers in the adult learning field and has had a considerable impact on the design and development of further and higher education, community education and practice in lifelong learning.

In PDP, both the 'what' and the 'how to' of learning are important. This means it's important to be aware of the learning methods that best suit you. Are you someone who prefers to learn in a group situation or alone? Do you learn more by reading or by researching on the internet? Do you like to debate with others or do you find this irritating or distracting when you're trying to learn? This 'learning how to learn' is sometimes called 'metacogniton'.

What suits you best in learning?

Learning about your own learning is highly relevant when it comes to deciding on the best way of achieving your development goals. You might be reading this book because you are undertaking the LDAF Higher Diploma, or a similar qualification, having decided that this qualification will help you in your career and work practice. If you're a LDAF candidate, you'll also be studying other mandatory units and will have selected your optional units. So, your study for the diploma or other qualification will feature strongly in your development plan. Reading this book and undertaking the activities (looking at websites, further reading, trying things out in work, comparing notes with colleagues) will constitute some of the methods you are currently using to achieve your development goals. But you will also have other development goals which do not involve LDAF study.

The learning method you choose will depend on a number of things: the nature of the goal, the time, resources and support available to you and your own preferences. For example, if one of your goals in the area of 'staff management and leadership' is 'to acquire better strategies for managing staff conflict', you have several learning options (or combination of options):

- go on a course or a workshop

- have someone (an 'expert') come in to advise you

- do some planned reading

- explore the internet for articles

- work out a plan with a more experienced colleague

- set up a staff working group to research the issue

Your learning would involve both *knowledge* and your *skills* and you'd have to apply what you learned in practice, which would lead to more learning – finding out what works and what doesn't, how you need to adapt things and so on. You'd probably use a number of different learning strategies, both *formal*, eg a course, and *informal*, eg reflection and discussion.

Resources, workload and life outside work also affect the learning methods you choose. Can you spare the time to go on a course? If a course costs £300 and you could learn the same things from reading a book costing £9.99, can you justify the course and would your organisation agree? To what extent do you have control over your own training budget? All part of development planning.

I've mentioned *formal* and *informal* learning. Formal learning strategies are generally planned, structured and deliberate, usually involve either a tutor or facilitator, are either face-to-face or done with computer, telephone or tutorial support. They include things like:

- short courses or workshops

- open or distance learning

- e-learning

- structured reading

- studying for a particular qualification

- work-based group learning – bringing in a specialist to run training in a specific area, eg challenging behaviour, mental health needs, relationships and sexuality

- undertaking research

- writing articles for journals

- producing training materials

- running training courses for staff or family carers

- attending or contributing to conferences or lectures

Informal learning strategies include such things as:

- setting time aside to reflect on your own practice as discussed in chapter 1

- writing a learning journal or log, or keeping a CPD portfolio

- deputising or covering for colleagues

- mentoring and/or training other staff

- visiting other services to find out how they do things

- chairing committees or working groups

- assuming new responsibilities

- learning from a colleague who is more experienced or knowledgeable in a particular area – wordprocessing or using the internet, for example

- establishing 'quality circles' in the workplace

It used to be that formal learning was more highly valued than informal learning and most emphasis was on paper qualifications. Qualifications still count for a lot, but we are increasingly realising the real value of informal learning. As long ago as 1961, Carl Rogers, well known for his work on experiential learning and person centred psychotherapy, contended that, 'The only learning which significantly influences behaviour is self-discovered, self-appropriated learning' (p. 276). The line between formal and informal learning has increasingly become blurred and the importance of 'lifelong learning' recognised. Gustafsson and Fagerberg (2004), writing about professional development for nurses, highlight the importance of self-insight and self-awareness, saying, 'Lifelong learning is a prerequisite in a profession that is in constant change, enabling professionals to be prepared for these changes' (p. 272). McNamara (1999) points out that most learning is informal and self-directed, but that learning is most powerful when it is systematic. Thus we have to plan our learning as thoroughly as we plan other things.

Learning opportunities nowadays are more flexible than they ever were. Continuing Professional Development (CPD) has become a recognised and required joint responsibility of the organisation and the employee. Your PDP should include both formal and informal learning opportunities – possibly those you may not previously have considered to be learning, such as involvement in training others or in mentoring.

Managers I spoke to talked about the benefits of the learning they were undertaking for Level 4 study, not only because of the structured aspects of the training, but also the other opportunities the training led them into, eg shared reflection and learning, further reading and research.

'Certainly in terms of some areas that have been crucial in terms of support we had to do quite a bit of research around dementia in relation to people with Down's syndrome, and that was proactive. We accessed a number of things through the web – mostly Stirling University – and that was something that we did openly, in respect of a tenant's support needs and also around the area of self-harm. It was kind of initiated in terms of myself and my deputy, who did the bulk of it. We did speak to psychologists who were involved in developing materials, but I kind of accessed some of the websites I knew around the stuff.'

'Similarly for some of the mental health issues that affected individuals within the project – and we have accessed some stuff – maybe somebody's given us a website address. Just thinking of some of the day-to-day stuff we use – I'm not sure it's formal research, like we've just learned today that over the course of the past four or five weeks a service user we have paired with the same support worker on a regular basis at the same times each week, in order to try and build up a relationship there, and reviewing that and being aware

working – you say, well, we've spoken to this person about it, they've expressed
et's just look for an alternative. So going back over the incidents that had taken
ecause we had done quite a lot of evidential gathering at that particular time,
ng the evidence from that in terms of informing what your decision might be it's
lusive, it possibly is inconclusive at the moment, so we will continue to monitor that
e'll continue that as research for our decision-making.'

e of the kind of most positive things about it [Level 4 training] was that we met
e day per month as a group in order to look at the work that was being done, look at the
ork we had to do ahead and to go over that work and to think about, you know, where
would you find that in your work, have you encountered that before, what did you do –
had you not encountered it before, what would you do in that situation – what options
are around it...'

'One of the most useful aspects of that was just the sharing. It was the fact that you then
actually had to think about what you do and why you do it that way. And probably, for me,
it made me much more aware of what I do. And that has been a bit of development that
I feel helped me in general in terms of the job. We did come up against some quite, you
know, some real challenges around actual practice which we all fall into, but you actually
need that challenge to say what can I do to change. I felt personally and professionally
developed. But I do have a worry that you don't get a lot of opportunities, unless you take
them yourself.'

To counteract this shortage of opportunities these same managers have established
a support group for themselves where they get together regularly to share common
concerns, ideas and approaches.

'We get together and discuss things. Then you've got peer support and you can look at
things. And you think, well, I'm not doing that in the way that I should. I can learn there's
another way of doing things – you know, there are just those sorts of opportunities that
we've had to create for ourselves, that are not created elsewhere.'

Development support from other managers, and from your line manager,
is particularly crucial in relation to complex situations, such as the one
described below.

'I'm thinking of an example recently when a woman we support said she and her partner
wanted to start a family – both have learning difficulties, the woman has siblings with
learning difficulties – and not really feeling that the woman understood the possible
consequences of this. They saw it as their right as individuals and adults within a
relationship, not particularly a loving relationship in the eyes of most people, but

having a right to pursue that course of action. Going along with the feelings that you have – expressing that to your line manager – I would say that all the feelings I had were acknowledged and agreed with, but there was the counterbalance to say, well, this is what we still have to do. You may have those feelings because you thought the relationship would fall apart, based on what we know about the relationship, because of the pressures of having a baby, particularly if the baby had a learning difficulty; good chance that the baby might have been removed from the home, the consequences of that on the woman in particular would have been catastrophic – being able to express all those feelings and having them respected, but at the same time being asked to consider the legalities and the moral issue in terms of what the person had the right to expect, that was OK. I didn't feel in any way my feelings were ignored. They were acknowledged and there was a fair amount of empathy with the way I felt. But also having a counterbalance for my feeling, because I was very emotional about it, really scared for the woman, really frightened of the consequences, but being reminded of having to be aware of the legal aspects and also your duty to the individual. Having that balanced was the right thing, I think. I am happy that feelings are acknowledged in support situations like that.'

The managers identified some organisational development events they had found particularly useful.

'[The organisation] ran a training event during our time of deregistration. It was an open space – they employed somebody to run it – it was a very useful day; I thoroughly enjoyed it. Basically all of the managers were invited. There was no agenda set for the day; we were asked to go along and anyone who felt strongly enough about something – stick it up on the board. If there were enough individuals interested in the same topic you would sign up for a time when there would be a group of you available to discuss it. I think over the course of the day I was involved in four different topics.'

'The person who put up the topic was responsible for facilitating the discussion. Salient points were recorded and at the end of the training day there was a record made of the responses to each point. I found that useful. You were with your peer group – that was very helpful. There was support that's important to us – a big part of what you need is just somebody there to listen to you at times, and empathise. Not all of the points that were raised had an answer to them, but at least there was an acknowledgement of, yes, this is where we are and we will just have to work through it. But being able to share your frustrations, problems, answers – it was having the space to do that.'

'It was an information gathering opportunity as well. It was all written up and sent out to people. It has been talked about. There was a recognition of the benefit – everybody who made the effort to attend got a lot out of it. But I suspect there is a cost aspect to it.'

These managers would also have welcomed the opportunity to be involved in the training of other people in more formal organisational events. They saw this as a prime development opportunity for themselves.

'Being invited to participate in activities like that, getting the opportunity to participate in training, somebody asking you to produce something for training – and having a go at doing that. That would be a good professional development opportunity.'

They had this advice to offer other managers about personal and professional development:

'Be aware of your own limitations. Maybe limitations isn't the right way to say it, although I think you should be aware of your own limitations because you end up getting sucked into situations you haven't time for really. I think if you can develop an awareness of your own limitations and also being aware of your strengths and weaknesses and whether you need to seek support from elsewhere. I think also the very basic thing – there's something wrong if you are having to take work home with you – there's either something wrong with the structure of your service or there's something wrong with the way you are doing the job. It is not beneficial at all. It certainly doesn't benefit you. And it certainly doesn't benefit your service. I think if people find themselves in that situation they really have to look at getting out of it. Not getting out of their job, but getting out of that situation.'

'The other bit as well is the opportunity to be involved in other things, for stimulation. Being invited to participate in activities, getting the opportunity to participate in [conducting] training, somebody asking you to produce something – and having a go at doing that. I think the other thing that probably is really missing is just having your thinking challenged on a regular basis.'

'In terms of support from the organisation – my own personal and professional development – I think for me the opportunity to just maybe look at developing some areas of interest I have, that are relevant to the job – and sometimes that is around using a lot of the experience you have in some quite complex support situations and in some quite complex support situations relating to workers as well – because I think quite often the most challenging part of the job is managing the individuals who support the people we support and I think there has to be some way of using the experience you gained to help other people to gain that insight as well. It's OK talking about it in theory, but actually being in really difficult situations where you are having to manage some difficult situations helps you have more of an insight than the theory. It's maybe about helping me develop the skills and confidence actually to be able to influence people's thinking in a wider perspective. It's also just being challenged more, to actually stretch your thinking.'

If your development plan is well thought out, implementation should, in theory, progress smoothly. The reality of practice, however, usually differs from the rhetoric and the learning options you choose will be influenced by such things as your workload, the availability of the resources you require, changes in your job role or in the way the organisation operates, to name only a few. When did you last miss a networking meeting or the second day of a workshop because of staff shortages or a crisis in your workplace? Before deciding on your learning options it makes sense to take another look at your development plan and decide on its viability. You might want to revise it, especially if your development goals are too ambitious. Remember, though, that it's expected that your plan will be adapted as time goes on and circumstances change, so new learning opportunities might become available.

Learning styles and the learning cycle

Bearing in mind that adult learners need to have control over their own learning – unlike children who have no choice about whether or not they go to school – there are two theories about learning that have particular relevance to this discussion. One, the *learning cycle*, casts light on the process of learning. The other, *learning styles*, relates, as its name suggests, to different ways of learning.

The learning cycle

David Kolb and Roger Fry (1975) created a diagrammatic representation of the learning process known as the cycle of experiential learning. This model of the learning process has been highly influential in the study and development of adult learning. Experiential learning, according to Kolb and Fry, involves:

- carrying out an action

- seeing the effect of this action in the particular situation

- understanding these effects (being thus enabled to anticipate the effects if the same action was to be carried out in the same situation again) and the general principles involved

- and being able to apply these in a new situation that has similarities with the first (generalising to other situations)

This process is represented thus:

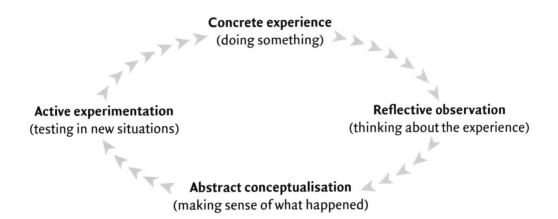

Kolb emphasises the role of experience in learning, something that is particularly relevant to adult learning and to PDP which relies on the experience professionals gain through their practice and on the need for continual reflection.

As we acquire new knowledge, so this new knowledge becomes embedded in our practice – we 'internalise' it. So, for instance, the experienced manager or senior practitioner visiting a tenant in a supported living household can 'get a feel for' how person centred a house is almost immediately, eg by the way staff and tenants relate, the language people use, the problems raised and so on. (This is Schon's *tacit knowing-in-action* discussed in chapter 1.)

Similarly, *reflection-on-action* (also Schon) can be related to the learning cycle – having done something, we reflect upon it, learn abstract lessons from it and apply these to a situation which bears similarities to the first, hoping for particular effects.

Kolb and Fry's experiential learning cycle has been adopted and developed by people in many different ways. At its simplest, it is often expressed thus:

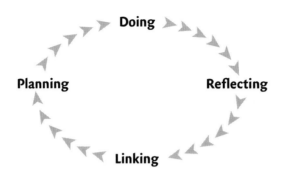

The process can be used to explain both formal learning, such as LDAF training, as well as the informal learning that occurs in everyday practice.

Learning styles

Kolb and Fry also developed an *inventory of learning styles*, based on the way adults perceive and process information. They contended that effective learning requires the possession of four different learning capacities (which correspond to the features of their learning cycle): concrete experience abilities, reflective observation abilities, abstract conceptualisation abilities and active experimentation abilities. Some people learn best from real life examples (concrete experience), while others prefer information presented as ideas (abstract conceptualisation). Once they have absorbed the information, some people prefer to do something with it (active experimentation), while others prefer to observe what's happening and reflect on it (reflective observation). Few of us possess the four styles equally (the ideal), but tend towards a particular dimension. The learning styles inventory places people on a line between concrete experience and abstract conceptualisation, and active experimentation and reflective observation. Thus four basic learning styles can be identified (Kolb, 1976):

Converger (abstract conceptualization + active experimentation)

- strong in practical application of ideas
- focuses on hypo-deductive reasoning on specific problems
- unemotional
- has narrow interests

Diverger (concrete experience + reflective observation)

- strong in imaginative ability
- good at generating ideas and seeing things from different perspectives
- interested in people
- has broad cultural interests

Assimilator (abstract conceptualisation + reflective observation)

- has a strong ability to create theoretical models
- excels in inductive reasoning
- concerned more with abstract concepts than people

Accommodator (concrete experience + active experimentation)

- strongest at doing things
- more of a risk taker
- performs well when required to react to immediate circumstances
- solves problems intuitively

You won't be surprised to hear that there has been considerable criticism of this theory of learning styles on many different fronts. Several critics condemn the theory as too simplistic. Webb (2003) has produced an extensive critique, with many challenges to the model. Among other things she says:

'It is apparent that the four separate modes depicted in Experiential Learning Theory are *not separate and distinct*. In fact, they are inextricably interconnected and interpenetrating. To suggest "learning requires abilities that are polar opposites and the learner, as a result, must continually choose which set of learning abilities he will bring to bear in any specific learning situation" (Kolb and Fry, 75:36) is to distort the findings and genius of Piaget, Kohler, Wertheimer, Jung, Dewey, and Lewin. The relationship between the four learning modes, at the least, must be described as reciprocal, interpenetrating, and functionally dependent' (http://cc.ysu.edu/~mnwebb).

Other criticisms are that:

- The model pays insufficient attention to the process of reflection (Boud et al, 1983).

- The experiential model of learning does not apply to all situations, so its claims are extravagant (Tennant, 1997).

- The model takes little account of cultural experiences and conditions (Anderson, 1988, cited in Tennant, 1997).

- The idea of stages does not reflect the reality of the way in which we think – the model is too simplistic.

- Empirical support for the model is weak (Jarvis, 1987; Tennant, 1997) – the initial research base was small and there have been few studies to test the model. Nor has the integration of the different learning styles been sufficiently explored.

- The relationship of learning processes to knowledge hasn't been sufficiently investigated or explained – the nature of knowledge and different ways of knowing haven't been explored adequately.

(based on Smith, M. K. (2001) http://www.infed.org/biblio/b-explrn.htm)

Despite all this, the work of Kolb and Fry has been influential in theories of adult learning, especially in relation to the role of experience in learning. So what does it all mean for your own learning? For a start, it should help you to get a clearer idea of your own strengths as a learner as well as weaknesses and to use this knowledge to plan your own learning more effectively. This should mean that the strategies you select to achieve your development goals are ones which suit your own approach to learning.

A number of other people have developed theories about learning styles since Kolb and Fry. Honey and Mumford (1982), for example, who also identified four learning styles:

- Activists, who learn best from new experiences and challenges, here and now tasks such as teamwork and problem solving, change and variety and high visibility activities such as leading discussions.

- Reflectors, who learn best from opportunities to watch and think, have time to think before acting, carry out detailed research, have time to review their learning and don't have time pressures or deadlines.

- Theorists, who learn best when there are systems, models, concepts and theories, can explore relationships between ideas, events and situations, analysis, evaluation and generalisation and can question basic assumptions or logic.

- Pragmatists, who learn best when there's a clear link between the problem and real life, when there are practical advantages, when they can emulate a model or concentrate on practical issues and when there's immediate opportunity to represent what they have learned.

Pask (1988) distinguished between holistic learners, who take a global view of what they're learning and make relationships between parts, and serialist learners who prefer a step-by-step approach.

Another distinction is between people who learn best through visual input, those who prefer auditory and those whose preference is kinaesthetic (hands-on) means.

Use the next activity to think about what kind of learner you are.

ACTIVITY 13: **Your own preferred learning style**

Look back at Kolb and Fry's learning styles and the characteristics that are associated with each. Which style most closely describes your approach to learning?

Next, look at Honey and Mumford's model and see if any of this relates to your own preferred way(s) of learning.

Finally, are you a visual, auditory or kinaesthetic learner? Or a combination?

Comment

Were you able to decide on one style or were you a mixture? One of the criticisms of the learning styles approach is that it pigeon-holes people and can limit opportunities. However, as learners we can adapt to different ways of learning, as you'll know from your own experience of having to adopt styles of learning you feel less drawn to. We shouldn't take it too seriously, but it can be helpful to point us in the direction of analysing our own preferred methods of learning.

You might like to...

...log on to http://www.ruby3.dircon.co.uk/Training%20Files/Theory%20Pages/intro.htm to find out more about theories of learning

---

Keeping track of your own learning

In PDP, it's important to monitor your learning so that you can see whether you're on track and identify any obstacles to learning. Monitoring can give you increased insight into your learning and improve your learning capacity. For example, using a learning styles approach, you might discover that you're losing motivation for private reading and would prefer to be in a shared and structured learning situation such as a course. To monitor your learning it helps to set down some markers – the timescale you've set yourself, for example. Are you on schedule? You might also plan your learning as a series of steps towards a particular goal, with the steps expressed as objectives. (The discussion on gap analysis in the previous chapter provides an example of how you might break your goal into a number of objectives which will enable you to monitor your progress more easily. You might want to look at it to remind yourself.)

It's easier to keep track of progress if your objectives are expressed accurately. You are probably familiar with the SMART formula for objectives (Specific, Measurable, Achievable, Relevant and Time-bound) which can be used in development planning, as in other work areas, as a way of helping to ensure that a plan is appropriate and progress assessable.

One of the most useful ways of keeping track of your own learning and development is by keeping a learning log or journal.

Learning journals

You may already be accustomed to keeping a journal, a diary or a portfolio, possibly as part of your own Continuing Professional Development. If you are a LDAF candidate, this journal of your own learning is the starting point for your LDAF assignment for this unit. Even if you aren't undertaking a LDAF qualification it's a good idea to keep a journal as this is invaluable in relation to appraisal, CPD and career progression. The journal should be kept in whatever format you feel comfortable with. Some people handwrite theirs while others prefer to get everything onto the computer. Sometimes it can be difficult to decide what to include and what to leave out in a journal. It can help to remember that the journal is *your own* working document, rather than a finished and polished product to which others have access.

Most people find that:

- It helps to get into a 'writing routine' as early as possible, although this might initially take some discipline.

- It's easier if you write up your journal regularly and as soon as possible after an event.

- The journal is particularly useful for structured discussion during supervision and mentoring activities.

What might your journal look like?

Think of your journal as a reflection of your ongoing learning, responses, feelings and discoveries. You might want to start with some notes to yourself of why you are keeping the journal, how you feel about doing it and what you hope to get out of it. This can get you started and it's helpful to look back and see whether your ideas or objectives change. Getting started can be daunting, so it's usually best just to launch yourself into it and write whatever comes to mind initially. For example:

'It's ages since I've written anything like this so I'm a bit nervous, but at least it's only for me. A bit worried about how I'll find the time to do it.'

'So this is my learning journal. Not sure about what I'll write in it or how it will help me but I usually write things down anyway to help me think so I suppose it's just an extension of that. Where to start – that's the question.'

'I'm a bit sceptical about this journal idea but I suppose it might help me to keep track of what I'm doing so I'm willing to give it a go. I wonder tho' if it's necessary to do it as well as reflective accounts – maybe it'll cut down on the work for the reflective accounts – we'll see!'

There will be plenty of time to reflect on your entries as your journal develops.

Your journal may reflect all aspects of your development plan, or might just contain an account of the learning activities you undertake and what you learned from them. You might include:

- short descriptions of different learning activities and their purpose

- feelings about particular events and experiences

- questions you want to ask yourself or other people about particular experiences

- comments on what went well, what didn't, why this might be so

- insights into particular aspects of your practice or learning

- notes on patterns you discern in your own learning and development

- problems identified and tackled, with outcomes

- notes on what you have learned

- suggestions for doing things differently or trying other options

You might write your journal as you would a diary, chronologically, or you might organise information under your different development goals. It's up to you to do it in a way that best suits you. You also need to decide how often you are going to write up your journal and be realistic about this. Some people prefer to spend a short time reflecting and recording at the end of their working day or shift, while others prefer to do this twice or three times a week. Remember that you also need to allocate time to look back over your journal to help you gauge progress and see patterns and links in your learning and development. There is no hard and fast rule apart from the fact that the more regularly you use your journal, the more useful you will find it.

Here is one example of what a journal or diary entry might look like. The extract is from a diary in which the manager is trying to promote the 'empowerment' of a group of tenants in a supported living scheme, according to the organisation's policy. The service is undergoing substantial change in the way it is provided and the tenants are being asked to play a major part in this. The manager wants to encourage them to be more forthcoming in their comments and ideas. The diary links to aspects of his development plan which have to do with 'managing change' and 'supporting staff and tenants in managing change'.

We (manager and deputy manager) met with the tenants' representatives again last night to discuss changes in the service and what it means for everybody. I wanted their ideas but I still feel they are taking their lead off the staff – that includes me but as well as the staff they meet every day who are influencing them I think. I really don't know how to change this. A few of them are outspoken but I still think they are just 'mouthpieces' for staff – What can we do about this? Need to think about it more and to talk to other managers who are going through the same thing to see how they're managing it. I really don't know if it's really possible for them to say what they think when we're there but how else can we do it – a problem! W. is very outspoken but that's another problem – Does he inhibit other tenants and are these his own feelings and ideas? How can I find out? Can I find out? I often wonder if empowerment really is possible for people who have been always told what to do or who find it difficult.

The diary goes on in this vein. You can see that the manager is identifying aspects of the problem, asking himself questions about possible root causes and thinking about some initial steps towards solutions. He is also grappling with a very complex and abstract concept – empowerment – which often appears in policy documents and mission statements but which then has to be translated into action in the real world. In addition, he also has to deal with radical change in service provision. Bringing all these elements together is challenging to say the least but is the reality of what managers often face. However, such change can also be energising and fulfilling, as these managers said:

'I think there was the ideal that was given to you, you know, that this is where we should be going, but I think the actual need to work that out, by and large came from yourself. I think there was the opportunity to check that out with various people, that does include basically your line manager, but also colleagues and services users – Do you think this is where we will end up? You know, like how you get there and stuff like that – and kind of take people through that process. And I think that type of development and learning was also very good, because I think you learned to reflect more. I mean even things like timescales, because you know you're thinking, right, we've got to do that, and some of the timescales that were placed upon the local authority were unusual. But I think you didn't really have an idea at that particular time of how long things would actually take. You know, if you thought it was going to take that length of time, you probably wouldn't have believed it. You would have thought you were going to be where you thought you were going to go much earlier. But again, a large exercise like that allows you much more of an opportunity to reflect on your practice, rather that the day-to-day stuff that you do, which is minutiae, if you like. If you've got this move where you've got to move from a registered service to a de-registered service, and looking at how you've done that and then what you've got in place it is very useful in terms of being able to reflect on your practice – Would you do it differently? Are you happy with what has been done? How did we get there? What knowledge underpinned how we got there? What were the values involved in how we got there? And are you happy with the values that continue to exist, having moved from that place to this? So that was a real practical opportunity to reflect on your practice.'

In the same discussion, another manager added:

'I would agree with that. And I also think the timing of it, when we de-registered, we had really started doing our SVQ in the November or the December, and we de-registered in the February, so de-registering brought about masses of stuff in terms of support opportunities for tenants. But that brought about major increases in staffing. We were trying to do the SVQ at the same time and it was high pressure. And I think when you're up against it, that's sometimes when you look at who you are as a person, and how that fits with your professional persona. It was quite painful, I think, but it was – I think, for a lot of people, we all reached our different highs and lows. But what I think it did do was it focused our thinking. You had no choice. You couldn't do it without thinking about it because you had time constraints on you, you had higher levels of demand on you and you had a lot more responsibility and accountability built into that. And I think that was a real learning curve. It was for me.'

In your diary or journal, you need not be concerned about writing style – notes, diagrams, drawings and so on are commonly used. Nor need you wait until the end of the day or your shift. Some people find it helpful to have a small notebook handy and jot things down as they occur to them. Perhaps you are one of those who already do this. Where possible, try to look on your journal as part of your practice instead of something separate. If you are accustomed to 'thinking on paper' you will find it easier to incorporate this into your daily practice routine. Here are a couple of extracts from such a notebook:

JH not there when I called – avoiding me because of what we need to discuss? How many times is this now – need to keep count.

Not happy about MM's attitude to service users – doesn't talk to them and is quite rough when she feeds them – need to talk to her and the agency.
(Refers to a relief member of staff from an agency in a service for people with profound and multiple learning disabilities.)

Journal entries that relate to the formal aspects of training, such as LDAF or S/NVQ, will have a different 'feel' from those relating to practice. Here's an example from someone studying a Level 4 unit. At this stage she is about a third of the way through the reading for the unit.

'I'm finding this unit really powerful. Hadn't thought too much about the history of learning disabilities before except in a general sense and don't know much about institutionalisation and all that. Really makes you think. What people went through. Some of the testimonies are heart-rending. Not sure what it means in respect of own work but it's things like power and control and society really and inclusion. But how to incorporate it into daily work? My own but also for other staff. All a bit fuzzy at the moment but need to think about it more. Would like to do a bit more reading about it but don't have time. Maybe will get clearer when I read more of the unit.'

Once she was further into the unit, this manager identified some of her insights into her current practice, some ways she could develop her own thinking, some steps she might take to improve both her knowledge and practice, and the problems she might face in doing this. Here are some of her diary comments:

'Realised how the service keeps people down without meaning to. This means me too. Do we really take them seriously. Like, we include them in some things but not in developing policies – all come from above. We (managers and staff) aren't involved enough either. We don't really know what's going on but we have to respond to 'their' demands? We need to be empowered too!

Decision: Talk to my line manager about this but also other service managers. This really needs to change!!!!

Thoughts: What else can I read about involving people more in making policy decisions? Who else has done it? Are there good examples? Has anybody else near here done it properly? Problems about sharing?

ACTIVITY 14: **Keeping a learning journal**

If you haven't already started keeping a learning journal, now is a good time to start. In your journal you need to keep a record of your learning and of how this increases your knowledge and affects your practice.

If you are a LDAF candidate, read through the assessment for this unit, which involves a reflective account in which you review the impact of the Higher Professional Diploma programme on your knowledge and practice. You'll see that it is suggested that you keep a learning log or journal of your learning and its application in the workplace.

Start by selecting one of the mandatory units. In your learning journal you should keep track of your progress through this unit. Do this by reflecting on what you learn by studying the unit and recording both what you learn and how this feeds into your practice.

If you are not a LDAF candidate you should select one or more of your development goals and keep track of your progress in terms of both knowledge and practice.

In your journal, you should include things like:

- new knowledge acquired as you study the unit

- insights you gain into your own practice as a result of your study/ learning/practice experience

- insights into your own preferred ways of learning

- questions that occur to you as you read over your notes

- ideas you want to try out

- further information you want to obtain and where you might get this

- instructions to yourself

- issues you want to discuss with your supervisor

- comments from your supervisor which you want to explore further or remember

- insights from other people which relate to your practice

- quotations which strike you as you read

- and whatever else will contribute to your own learning and development

Comment

The best time to get started on your journal is now – if you haven't already done so. You'll need to be disciplined about it. If you are, you'll soon get into the habit and you will probably be surprised at what you learn from it. If you have colleagues who are also keeping learning journals you might like to get together to discuss them. However, you may prefer to keep it private. It's up to you. There is no correct way of writing a learning journal. What's important is that it suits *you*.

Some people prefer to keep a portfolio rather than a journal, although the distinction between the two is not always clearly defined. In general terms, a portfolio is likely to be a more comprehensive document. Whereas a learning log or journal may be confined to reflective accounts of an individual's learning and development, a portfolio will contain additional information. Thus, if you were to keep a portfolio which only deals with your PDP you would include everything relating to your development plan – all the stages discussed in the last chapter and this – as well as records of meetings with your facilitator, supervision records, attendance and completion certificates from courses and so on. As with all aspects of PDP there is no hard and fast rule. Your organisation may prescribe what you do and why or may leave it up to you and your facilitator or supervisor. On the other hand, your portfolio might be even more comprehensive than this, eg have your job description, your CV, your year-on-year development records and so on, as required by the organisation as a record of your CPD. The more comprehensive the document, the greater the need for good organisation of information. Organisations vary in the extent to which they have developed their PDP processes and your records will reflect this.

Reviewing your learning and your development plan

This ongoing reflection on your learning is invaluable for your PDP review. Approaches to review differ as much in PDP as they do in other aspects of professional life – some are highly formalised while others are left up to the preferences of employees. Reviews should enable you to:

- reflect critically on your own development
- build a fuller picture of your own values, capacities and knowledge
- express your feelings about your progress, opportunities and problems in an honest and supportive environment
- obtain additional support where necessary
- appraise your own progress, your value to the organisation and your role in contributing to the development of the organisation

---

ACTIVITY 15: **PDP review**

Use the Internet to find at least three examples of approaches to Personal Development Planning. Look particularly at the process and format they use for review.

If your organisation has a standardised format for review, compare it with the ones you have found on the Internet. What are the strengths and weaknesses of each?

If your organisation doesn't yet have a standardised procedure and format, could the examples you have found help you to devise one? If so, how?

Comment

Whatever your approach to learning, it's always useful to see examples of the way other people do things. I always think of these as 'stimulus materials' which help me develop my own thinking. There's so much available nowadays, particularly through the Internet. If you do find something that is useful to your organisation, don't forget about copyright laws.

Concluding comments

Learning is such an integral part of professional life that it's impossible to avoid it even if we wanted to. Understanding your own approaches and preferences is important, not least because it helps you capitalise on your strengths and interests. Motivation is a prime trigger for learning. The better you know yourself, the more you will understand others – an essential feature of leadership.

One of the most productive methods of learning is through involving yourself in action research – one of the topics I move on to in the final chapter. I also discuss the importance of keeping up to date with research and legislation and integrating new developments into practice.

Chapter 4

Integrating new developments into practice

Introduction

At the present time, services for people with learning disabilities are probably changing more fundamentally than they ever have. All of the UK policy documents – *Valuing People, The same as you?, Fulfilling the Promises* and *Equal Lives* – highlight the need for substantial changes in services and in practice. Hospital closures and community interventions mean that people who have been denied their basic rights for so long are at last returning to their own communities. Person centred approaches to practice are starting to have an effect. These and similar developments are encouraging, but the struggle for inclusion and full citizenship for people with learning disabilities still has a long way to go.

All this is promising and long overdue, but it also makes it critical – and challenging – for you as a manager or senior practitioner to keep up to date with all the changes. You have a responsibility to people with learning disabilities and their families, but also a leadership role within your service, a commitment to your own professional development and accountability to the organisation – all of which have to be reconciled with one another. This makes it imperative for you to keep up to date with legislation, policy and research and to implement relevant aspects of these in practice.

In this final chapter I focus on this responsibility for keeping yourself well informed about research and legislation and for integrating new developments into practice. In particular, I explore the following issues:

- keeping your own knowledge and practice up to date and supporting others to do this

- using external networks to inform and challenge your practice and to obtain support during a crisis

- learning from research

- integrating relevant legislation and research into practice

Keeping your knowledge and practice up to date

How do you make sure that you keep your knowledge and practice up to date? Answer this question by doing the next activity.

ACTIVITY 16: **Keeping up to date**

Which of the following activities do you use to keep up to date with legislation and research? Tick the ones which apply.

☐ reading professional books and journal articles

☐ subscribing to a professional journal

☐ meetings of a professional body

☐ being part of several networks: local; national; international

☐ subscribing to and using an academic library

☐ reading organisational circulars

☐ writing circulars for the organisation

☐ taking part in research projects: local; national; international

☐ frequent use of the Internet

☐ attending courses and workshops

☐ running courses and workshops

☐ attending conferences

☐ contributing to conferences

Add others not on this list which you are involved in.

Which of those listed above are most useful and why?

What else could you make a commitment to do that you don't do already?

Give a date for when you will make a start on these additional activities.

Comment

Pressures of work can make it difficult to keep up to date, can they not? But if this is something that happens to you, you might want to think of ways to address the root cause. Do you need more support, for example? Could your workload be decreased or reorganised? Could you organise yourself better? If you have a personal development plan, activities for keeping up to date with research and legislation should be built in, so this is one way of trying to ensure that they happen. If there are problems who can you talk to about this and what kind of support do you need?

The UK policy documents I mentioned in the introduction to this chapter have identified the changes which need to take place in support services for people with learning disabilities. To what extent have these policy documents influenced your practice? Answer this question by doing the next activity.

ACTIVITY 17: **How policy affects practice**

Read through *Valuing People* if you work in England, *Fulfilling the Promises* if in Wales, *Equal Lives* if you are in Northern Ireland, or *The same as you?* if you are in Scotland. Identify the objectives or recommendations which have had most influence on your work and read what is written in the relevant section in the document.

Describe the ways in which your work has changed or is changing as a result of these recommendations.

If the recommendations have had little or no effect on your work, should they have and, if so, why haven't they?

Now log on to the *Valuing People* website (www.valuingpeople.gov.uk), the website of the Scottish Consortium for Learning Disability (www.scld.org.uk), Mencap Northern Ireland (www.mencap.org.uk/download/equal%2olives.rtf) or www.wales.gov.uk and find out about current developments in your area. Make a note of the ones which apply to your own work. Are you involved in any of them? If so, what is your role and how is this informing your practice?

Comment

Your answers to these questions will be related to the previous activity and the extent to which you are involved in effecting change in your own organisation. The changes outlined in the documents provide opportunities for substantial development. Logging on to the websites regularly is a fairly straightforward way of keeping up to date with developments, so if it isn't already a part of your routine it's a good idea to make it.

Using external networks to inform and challenge your practice and to obtain support during a crisis

One very effective way of improving practice is the creation and use of networks. Some networks have existed for a long time but others have resulted from the reviews of support services mentioned in the activity above. This increase in networking is a welcome development. One of the reasons why so many people with learning disabilities were excluded, neglected, exploited or abused is that they lived in segregated communities with no interaction with the outside world. Our traditional approach to both day and residential care was to provide separate services which kept people with learning disabilities apart from mainstream society. It was easy, therefore for neglect and abuse to occur. Even in services in which people were well cared for, the tendency was often towards protection rather than inclusion. It is only in the last thirty years that real change – like hospital closures – has started to happen. The movement towards inclusion started small, mainly through pioneering work of individuals and campaigning groups such as Value into Action (originally called the Campaign for Mentally Handicapped People – CMH), but has gathered momentum. Righting the wrongs of exclusion and oppression will take a long time, but the more links services have with ordinary social networks, the more quickly change will happen.

External networks take a variety of forms:

● local community and citizen networks such as neighbourhood watch schemes and tenants organisations

● local committees

● professional bodies, eg National Network for Learning Disability Nurses, PMLD Link

● inter-professional networks with a particular purpose, eg reviewing developments in policy implementation

- learning networks and special interest groups which meet on a voluntary basis

- support networks such as circles of support

- formally constituted networks such as those established by social services/ social work departments

- networks accessed online, bulletin boards and chat rooms

Networks are useful for keeping you up to date with developments by:

- informing you

- showing you how other people have implemented policy and legislation

- enabling you to be part of, and feed into, working groups, committees, policy-making bodies and similar

- giving you the opportunity to respond collectively to policy changes and legislation and to shape the future

- helping you learn more about the community in which you work

Networks can enable you to challenge your own practice by:

- learning how other people do things

- helping you become involved in 'communities of practice' which reflect on, and make changes to, the way things are done

- exposing you to other perspectives

Networks can help you obtain support in crisis situations through:

- having a clearer idea of what support is available outside your own organisation

- building bridges with community members and organisations

- having ready access to different kinds of support and the people providing it

- being informed about how other people deal with similar situations and drawing on their experiences

Networks reduce isolation and give you opportunities to share ideas with like-minded people. They also help your organisation to be more transparent and accountable.

ACTIVITY 18: **Support from networks**

Give an example of a network you have found useful and describe its usefulness to you in terms of:

● increasing your knowledge

● improving your practice

Comment

In the resources section of this book you will find a list of online networks and organisations which you might find useful in networking.

Learning from research

Another important influence on practice is research, especially that which is grounded in practice. How do *you* feel about research? Perhaps you feel that it is something other people do that has little impact on your work. Do you, as Padak and Padak (undated) remark, have preconceived notions of your own ability to do research, question its usefulness, think the process has to be highly technical, that researchers have little to offer the real world? Or perhaps you've been involved in research yourself – possibly are at this moment. Maybe, like me, your feelings about research can be summed up as, 'Well, it all depends...'. This kind of feeling is fine, I feel, because it makes us question the way research is undertaken and the conclusions that are drawn from it.

In this section, I want to consider two aspects of research. The first concerns ways to constructively challenge research. The second involves action research which I feel is the kind of research most relevant to practice. After doing this, I want to consider how you can evaluate the relevance of research and legislation and implement it in your own workplace.

Challenging research constructively

If research is seen as something 'out there', the domain of 'experts', then there's little chance of ordinary people like you and me feeling that it has anything to do with us. If, however, we believe that we *should* have a stake in research – and that people with learning disabilities and their families should have too – we are much more likely to become informed about research and to challenge research findings we don't feel happy with. To do this, we need to have a firm base from which to proceed. We might challenge research if:

- People with learning disabilities are treated as objects or 'subjects' rather than unique individual people.

- The research is out of line with the social model of disability, eg focuses on a person's 'deficits' rather than his or her ability and humanity; is geared towards segregation rather than inclusion.

- The voices of people with learning disabilities, family carers and/or advocates are not represented, eg self-advocacy is researched without the involvement of people with learning disabilities.

- The research is unethical in any way, eg might have adverse effects on people, be exploitative or intrusive, support a negative or deficit view of people with learning disabilities.

- It uses exclusive or pejorative language or concepts.

- Findings from one small group of people are extrapolated to everyone with learning disabilities, all practitioners, all managers or all family carers.

- The research is biased, eg only findings that suit the hypothesis are accepted and other findings ignored; the people involved are not representative in relation to the issue being investigated. (I was interested the other evening in television interviews with people about the possibility of introducing congestion charges in Edinburgh. All except one of those questioned were professional people with high-paying jobs in the city.)

- The research purports to be about one thing but focuses on something different – it's acceptable for the direction of a research study to change, but this change must be explained and the findings reflect it.

Activity 19: **Challenging research constructively**

Read *Doing Research – And Doing It Right, A Community Fund Guide to Ethical Aspects of Research Grants Applications* by Linda Ward and Debby Watson, for the Community Fund (www.c-f.org.uk/about-us/our-publications/research-grants/research-guide.pdf).

List the main messages in this guide.

Action research – some background information

Action research goes under many names. Sometimes it's called just action research, sometimes 'participatory research' and sometimes 'participatory action research'. I want to say something first about the 'participatory' aspect of this kind of research, which I believe is crucial.

Just as our perception of support services has changed, so has our stance on research. Once, research was something largely divorced from practice (too much still is!), carried out by other people and often inaccessible. Research was based on a scientific model. People were 'subjects' and research was done *to* them. Some research still happens like this, of course, but we're learning gradually that this approach is inappropriate in social care and related fields. There's now much more emphasis on participatory research, not least because it recognises people with learning disabilities as people, rather than objects. Tilakaratna (1990) says, 'Participatory Research seeks to de-elitise and de-mystify research thereby making it an intellectual tool which ordinary people can use to improve their lives.' and, 'Participatory Research must be sharply distinguished from conventional Elitist Research which treats people as objects of the research process' (Tilakaratna, 1990).

There must be real participation, not just tokenism. Participatory research is more than just including quotes from people with particular experiences or bringing them in now and then to provide some sort of credibility. It means involving the people concerned from the outset, from identifying the issues and designing the research approach to deciding on and trying out the solutions. To be truly participative, research must be based on real partnership and be an interactive process from beginning to end. It is about empowerment and helping people make their voices heard.

Participatory research challenges the idea of the outside 'expert'. Todhunter (2001) writes:

'It is democratic and participatory by nature and is in sharp contrast to the positivistic "top-down" approach which has been accused of "lifting decisions from the village square" and placing them with "experts or outside agencies" (Bryant, 2001). The practice goes by many names: community-based research, participatory research, collaborative research, and others, but rests on two main principles: democratization of the knowledge process, and social change (Stoeker, 1996)' (http://www.soc.surrey.ac.uk/sru/SRU34.html).

Action research is sometimes described as one of a family of approaches. Dick (1999) for example, describes it as 'a family of research methodologies which pursue action (or change) and research (or understanding) at the same time' and also as 'an emergent process which takes shape as understanding increases; it is an interactive process which converges towards a better understanding of what happens'. Theoretically, it is possible – although highly unusual – to conduct action research on your own by undertaking critical enquiry of your own practice.

I'm inclined to believe that action research is only really useful if it is participatory, so my premise is that 'action research' implies the participation of the people who are most centrally concerned. This might be people with learning disabilities, family carers, other practitioners or other stakeholders.

A simple explanation of action research is that it makes a direct link between research and action. It is concerned with change. We can draw parallels with reflective practice, as discussed in the first chapter, and described by Cook (2004) as 'a continuous cycle in which you select an area of your work to investigate, collect information about it, reflect upon, then perhaps develop new ideas about ways of working and act upon those' (p. 80).

In action research, there is no 'perhaps' – new ideas and ways of doing things are integral.

McMahon (1999) poses the question: 'Is reflective practice synonymous with action research?' and answers 'emphatically not' (p. 167), pointing out that action research involves strategic action. Such action might result from reflective practice but is not an integral part of it. But reflective practice and action research are closely allied. McMahon concludes: 'the strategic dimension is not only the most valid distinguishing feature but also the key to an understanding of how the two can be usefully related in practice. Reflective practice can help to identify problems, action research can seek to provide solutions' (p. 168). Reflection plays a key role in action research. Leitch and Day (2000) contend that there has been insufficient attention paid to the nature of reflection in action research and its relationship to purposes, processes and outcomes. The more experienced you are in reflective practice, the better equipped you are for action research. Action research also takes significant account of values, something that, as Bannister and Remenyi (1999) point out, is unquestioned in traditional research.

Leitch and Day (2000) talk of 'different kinds of action research' (p. 179) and 'different orientations of action research' (p. 183). They cite Grundy's (1982) distinction between technical (emphasis on technical skill), practical (improving practice through practical judgement and practical wisdom) and emancipatory (directed towards changing social systems) models of action research. Some people dispute this division, especially with regard to 'technical' action research, contending that research is only truly action research if it is emancipatory. However, there is also wide agreement that emancipatory action research is extremely challenging, directed as it is towards substantial social change. Thus action research, especially on a small scale, often results in changes in practice that combine the technical and the practical, rather than any kind of emancipation, as described by Walker in her work with teachers in South Africa. She also comments on how her understanding of action research changed and developed through involvement and continues to do so and believes that there is no essential or absolute that constitutes action research, remarking: 'the search is not for right answers but towards "practical wisdom ... in particular, complex and human situations" (Elliott, 1991, p. 52 in Walker, 1993, p. 107)'. This developing understanding of the nature and process of action research is a commonly experienced one and challenges the need for an 'expert' researcher, although experience of action research and its methods is obviously beneficial.

Dick and Swepson (1997) describe action research as 'a research paradigm which allows you to develop knowledge or understanding as part of practice', useful for improving understanding of practice and useful for 'involving clients as co-researchers'. They point out that it is useful for exploratory purposes when you do not have a precise research question, but most valuable when you have to respond to changing demands of situations, and want to build a research element into it, which makes it particularly relevant to today's developments in the field of learning disability. Dick (1997) reports how he and a colleague set out to devise a minimal definition of action research but found this difficult and settled on two main criteria for action research, namely that it:

- pursues both action and research outcomes

- is a cyclical process, with critical reflection involved in each cycle and is usually qualitative and participative (but they preferred to leave these as choices)

Action research has its origins in the work of Kurt Lewin and his associates in the late 1930s. Lewin was particularly concerned with raising the self-esteem of minority groups, encouraging independence, equality and co-operation and overcoming exploitation and colonialisation. What was required, Lewin held, was collective research on 'private (shared) troubles' involving reflective thought, discussion, decision and action by ordinary people (Adelman, 1993). This occurs as ongoing cycles of action and reflection, the lessons learned from one cycle feeding into, and transforming, the next in a continuing spiral. Lewin represented this as a spiral of steps:

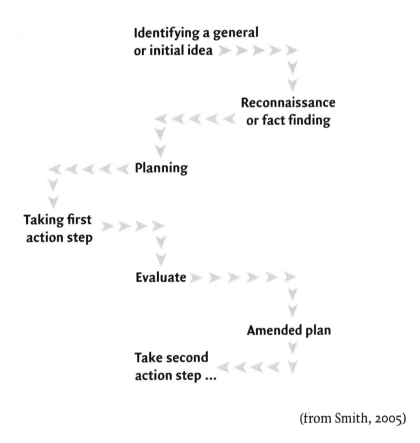

(from Smith, 2005)

Lewin's spiral has been adapted in many different forms. At its simplest, it is often represented as follows:

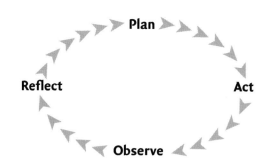

You will notice that there are similarities here with Kolb's cycle of experiential learning.

Coghlan and Brannick (2001) use the following spiral of action research cycles to illustrate the process:

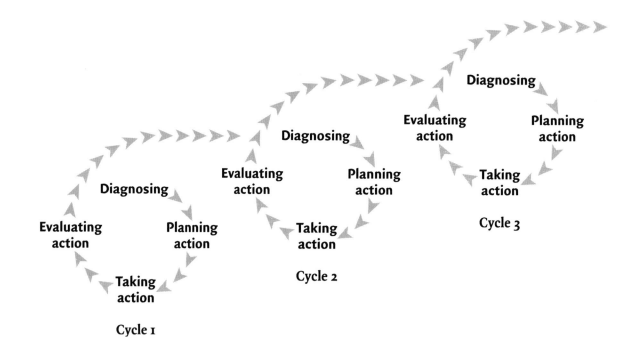

Stringer (1999) describes three basic phases in action research:

'Look – building a picture and gathering information. When evaluating we define and describe the problem to be investigated and the context in which it is set. We also describe what all the participants (educators, group members, managers, etc) have been doing.

Think – interpreting and explaining. When evaluating we analyse and interpret the situation. We reflect on what participants have been doing. We look at areas of success and any deficiencies, issues or problems.

Act – resolving issues and problems. In evaluation we judge the worth, effectiveness, appropriateness and outcomes of those activities. We act to formulate solutions to any problems.'

The slogan that came to characterise Lewin's approach was: 'No action without research; no research without action'. This has echoes in such sentiments as: 'Nothing about us without us' which has been adopted by different groups of disabled people, including those with learning disabilities. Thus action research is particularly suited to work with people with learning disabilities, implying as it does that the people concerned are central to the process right from the start. Adleman (1993) states: 'Action research must include the active participation by those who have to carry out the work in the exploration of problems that they identify and anticipate' (p. 9). He adds a word of caution, contending that some advocates of action research make inflated claims for its impact on practice and policy while others focus too much on individual development to the detriment of the group and the organisation.

There's a large body of information about action research, far more than I have scope for here. I have merely outlined some of the issues I feel are most relevant, either to refresh your memory, if you already use action research, or to whet your appetite. In the Resources section of this book there are publication and website references which should be useful in augmenting your own knowledge of action research.

People with learning disabilities and action research

The next activity should add to your understanding of action research and people with learning disabilities.

ACTIVITY 20: **Reading about action research**

Get hold of an article describing action research and people with learning disabilities and/or family carers and/or staff working in a support service with people with learning disabilities, preferably one which has some relevance to your own work. To help you, use the list of journals in the Resources section of this book, the Internet, an academic library or BILD Information Services or Current Awareness Service. Read the article and carry out the following tasks.

Summarise the article as if you were writing an abstract for it.

What research methods were used?

Describe the process and the outcomes of the research

Evaluate the research by answering the following questions:
How (a) useful and (b) effective was the research?

What are the implications of this research for practice?

What were the limitations and/or shortcomings of this research?

Comment

Did you have any difficulty in finding a suitable research article? Although the use of action research with people with learning disabilities is relatively new, it is increasing. There are many challenges, especially when researching with people with more severe learning disabilities and profound and multiple learning disabilities. This in itself is formative to all of us as a 'learning community' as it forces us to find new inclusive ways of doing things. Communication is particularly important. Many of the strategies used by the self-advocacy movement and in the involvement of service users in policy-making, staff selection and interviewing and person centred planning can be adapted for use in action research, so there is no reason why there shouldn't be an increase in the use of action research at service and organisational level.

You might like to think about...

...the different ways in which action research might be useful to you in your own practice

...the challenges you would face in undertaking action research

...if action research could be part of your networking activities

...if there are examples of action research in your community, with groups other than people with learning disabilities that you could learn from

...if there are action research projects in your local community that should involve the perspectives of people with learning disabilities, but don't, and how you could change this

Naturally, the best way of finding out about action research is to get involved in it, which is what I now move on to.

Doing action research

Whether you are already experienced in action research or whether it is new to you, it's always worth doing, not least because it casts new light on practice. Because of its flexibility, action research lends itself well to support work with people with learning disabilities and their families. However, there are some issues we need to be aware of. The first is an obvious one – the methods used must suit the people participating and this can pose challenges when those involved have learning disabilities.

Fortunately, many of the strategies we use in alternative and augmentative communication, in total communication, in self-advocacy and in person centred planning can also be employed in action research, with or without adaptation. For example:

- oral history

- life story books

- pictures, signs and symbol systems, such as Makaton or Talking Mats

- devices used in meetings, such as different coloured cards to signal particular things, 'traffic lights'

- mapping, such as mobility mapping (where I spend my time), social mapping (who's who in my life)

- graphics to indicate likes and dislikes, feelings about different things and so on

- social stories

People who communicate verbally can also use interviews, focus groups and discussion.

Currently there is considerable debate over the role of the nondisabled researcher in so-called 'inclusive' research, not least around the issues of power, control and equality. Walmsley (2004), exploring the role of the nondisabled researcher, suggests that inclusive disability research has been driven by values of social justice and the desire to redress wrongs and promote valued social roles rather than by an evidence base which helps us to understand the skills involved. Frequently, nondisabled researchers have failed to explain what they do and how they do it, so the role remains obscure. Greater transparency about the role is needed if we are to move forward with inclusive research and provide the training and support people on both sides of the partnership require – people with learning disabilities and career researchers. Walmsley also highlights our struggle with the language of research, saying: 'The binary divide, the polarising of "the nondisabled" and the "disabled", the "researcher" and the "co-researcher", the "inquirer" and "the expert" is perpetuated, not dissolved, through inclusive research' (p. 70). People with learning disabilities, she points out, do not need obscurest language to prove that they have made, and will continue to make, valuable input to research. Instead, they need 'the contributions they make to be named and described and recognised for what they are, not for what we wish they could be' (p. 71). Williams and Simons (2005) discuss the intricacies of people with and without learning disabilities doing research together, highlighting particularly the need for vigilance over issues of power and control and the fact that the nondisabled researcher is learning the trade along with everyone else. Questioning whether it is possible to be both a supporter and a researcher simultaneously, Williams suggests that the role might be described as 'researcher in residence' much in the same way as 'artist in residence', a description which identifies both the professional aspect of the role but also the fact that the nondisabled researcher is also there to learn and to contribute, like the researchers with learning disabilities.

You need to ensure that your approach takes account of these and related factors. Your research will also be determined by the nature of the problem or issue being investigated. Your research partners might be colleagues either in your own organisation or from other agencies, people with learning disabilities, family carers, volunteers, other community members or a combination of representatives of all stakeholders. The wider the range of perspectives and interests, the richer – but more demanding – the research, so you need to bear this in mind and not be too ambitious, especially in the initial stages.

You might like to read...

'More researching together: the role of nondisabled researchers in working with People First members' by Val Williams and Ken Simons (2005) in the *British Journal of Learning Disabilities* volume 33, pp. 6–14

'Inclusive learning disability research: the (nondisabled) researcher's role' by Jan Walmsley (2004) in the *British Journal of Learning Disabilities* volume 32, 2, pp. 65–71

If you base your research on Lewin's research cycle, your first step will involve identifying the issue you want to investigate. Because action research is so flexible, your question or problem need not be precise at this stage. It will become clearer as you develop your ideas and your research. So, for example, it might be:

- something as basic (but important) as a complaint that people using a day centre are bored

- the fact that several people in a supported living scheme need better day-to-day support

- that your organisation wants to improve user involvement in one or more aspects of the service

- about helping people newly moved out of hospital to renew contact with family members

- to improve the lives of people with profound and multiple disabilities newly moved into a house in the community

Almost anything that is perceived as a problem or as requiring change lends itself to action research.

The second step is for you and your co-researchers to collect information about the issue under investigation, using appropriate methods. This involves reflecting on the issue or problem and gathering information about it from all those involved. This can take a considerable amount of time and should be done in different ways to reflect different perspectives and dimensions of the issue, eg focus group discussions, graphics, visits to different places, structured or semi-structured interviews. All of these methods have advantages and disadvantages. Collecting information will almost certainly not be a one-off event.

Step three is to agree on the action that needs to be taken to resolve or improve on the situation, ie to generate ideas about different options, decide on the most appropriate and devise an action plan which clearly specifies the actions, who is responsible for what, the timescale, and resources and support needed. This action plan will change as each cycle progresses and the findings are fed back into the process. Monitoring procedures have to be agreed at this stage. Neither the plan itself nor the monitoring procedures need be unduly complicated. In fact, there is an argument for simplicity. Once things get too complex there's a greater chance of things going wrong. So monitoring might be about people meeting regularly to report back on developments and problems and the plan being changed to resolve the problems.

The next step is the implementation of the plan of action. Monitoring is part of the ongoing evaluation of your project, but you will also need to specify a date at which you want to have a more thorough evaluation. This might be because you have reached the end of the specified time period, or because the required change has happened or is partially achieved, or because circumstances have changed and the plan is now irrelevant. Or it might be that the plan just isn't working. Whatever the situation, questions need to be asked. I discuss this in more detail later in the chapter.

These cycles of planning – doing – reviewing continue as long as required. As you move on to subsequent cycles you refine your strategies while at the same time adding to your knowledge and understanding.

You'll have noticed that the cycle bears a strong resemblance to both the development planning cycle and the experiential learning cycle, which isn't surprising since all three are about learning. Your own action research will be an integral part of your PDP and of your own practice. You might decide to focus just on one of your development goals initially, or to pursue more than one simultaneously. This decision will be governed by the nature of the goals you've identified and the way the goals relate to one another. In the next activity, you can write about an action research project in which you are already involved, or in one you are planning to undertake.

ACTIVITY 21: **Action research project**

Give a brief description of your action research project.

Who are or will be your co-researchers?

Why are you doing this research and what do you hope to learn from it?

What methods will you use and why?

Comment

This action research should be something that fits easily into your own work practice. It may be a case of adapting something you already do – meetings with service users to review and plan aspects of the service; networking with colleagues from other services to plan training events – or similar activities. Your reflective diary will be useful for recording your own feelings, questions and insights. You need also to consider how to reflect on the changes in your own practice which result from the research, as well as the effects on the organisation as a whole. How will you disseminate your findings, for example?

Principles for evaluating your action research

The learning which emerges from your action research is only useful if it enables you to make changes in your own practice. So how can you get most from it? The key is, of course, evaluation. Evaluation in action research should, like all other parts of the process, be participatory. But, as Kemmis and McTaggart (1988) remark, research 'is only action research when it is collaborative, though it is important to realise that the action research of the group is achieved through the critically examined action of individual group members' (p. 5). Reflection on your own practice, as well as collective evaluation, therefore, is crucial. Similarly, you can contribute to other people's insights into their own practice. Perspectives from people with learning disabilities and family carers particularly can differ considerably from those of professionals and lead to enhanced understanding.

At the heart of evaluation is effective questioning. You need to ask the right questions, of the right people (including yourself), in the right way. You need to know what worked, what didn't, why or why not, what has been learned and what needs to be done differently next time. There are four main elements:

- Why are you evaluating (purpose)?

- What will you evaluate (process/outcomes)?

- When will you evaluate (timescale)?

- How are you going to do it (methods)?

Why are you evaluating?

Part of this is obvious – to see what worked, what didn't and what learning has emerged that can improve practice. But within this framework there may be other questions, such as:

- What has been achieved to date – where are we now and where do we go next?

- What problems and barriers did we encounter?

- Why was it that some things worked particularly well and others didn't? What are the strengths and how can we build on them? What are our weaknesses and how can we overcome them?

There will almost certainly be unexpected outcomes, since life is neither predictable nor controllable. Or we might want to strengthen something – networks, or the most positive aspects of a service, for example.

What will you evaluate?

In action research you need to evaluate process as well as outcomes as both need to be in the feedback loop if learning is to occur. In terms of process you might ask:

- Were all stakeholders represented – and did they have an equal say?

- Were methods suitable and accessible for everyone?

- How did different people feel about the methods we used?

- What were relationships like between different groups of stakeholders?

- How did things change as the research progressed, eg relationships, methods etc? What improved? What got worse?

- Has there been any lack of clarity about any parts of the process or about people's roles?

- What did participants like best about the methods used?

- What did participants not like about the methods used?

- What sorts of challenges have we encountered?

- What barriers have we met and have we overcome these? If so, how?
  If not, why not?

- Were there any 'critical events' that had a serious impact on the research?

- What have been the most common concerns?

- Was the timescale realistic?

- Did we come up against any problems in terms of ethics or values?

In relation to outcomes, you might ask:

- To what extent did we achieve our aims?

- How do we know this?

- What didn't we achieve?

- How did work practice change as a result of the research? What changed for the better and how? What changed for the worse and how?

- Who has been most affected by these changes and how?

- What kinds of evidence have we used to judge our results?

- Are there any differences of opinion about the outcomes? If so, what and whose? What are the messages from these?

- Have we had to rethink our aims? Have we changed direction and if so, is this acceptable?

Questions of this sort enable you to gather information and opinions about what is working, or has worked, well and what hasn't. I've given only a few examples – you will be able to think of many others. The information you gather as a result of the questions shows what needs to be changed and indicates how you might start doing this – or at least talking about it.

How will you evaluate?

Evaluation in action research needs to take account of both individual feedback and collective opinions. So, for example, feedback from family carers may be different from that from people with learning disabilities, and that from professionals might be different again. There may be points of contact but there will also be differences. Within the groups individual opinions will also differ. Evaluation methods must be robust and flexible enough to take account of these different opinions – consensus is not always necessary.

Individual reflection should feed into shared evaluation. Thus you might use a reflective diary or journal as a monitoring tool and feed information from this back into evaluation meetings.

There's a host of evaluation methods that can be used to assess developments in action research. The list below includes some of those more commonly used – you'll be able to add others.

- focus group discussion, either with an 'outside' facilitator or facilitated by the participants

- 'card-sorts' using small cards or adhesive notes to record relevant points and then sort these into categories, eg 'worked well', 'didn't work', 'OK but could be better'

- thinking aloud (free conversation) in pairs or small groups and recording these thoughts on tape

- recording diagrammatically, eg using 'mind maps', tree diagrams or flowcharts

- recording in pictures (graphics), eg pictures of 'good things', 'bad things', 'things that were OK'

- using a prepared framework with set questions which everyone answers from their own perspective

- assessing progress against predetermined indicators

- participants interviewing one another using a prepared schedule

- rating schedules, from basic to complex, eg like/OK/don't like; useful/not useful/don't know; rating things in order from best to worst

- mapping activities, eg social maps – how relationships are changing; location maps – how interaction with the community is changing; network maps; and so on

- timelines, eg what changed first/when, then what/when, then what and so on – these might develop into 'tree diagrams' as 'knock-on effects' are identified; these can also be used to project into the future – Where would you like to be in 1/2/3 years time? Where have you got to at the present time? – and so on

- observation – taking part in particular activities and having other participants observe and give feedback

- 'acting out' and 'simulated' activities such as sculpting and role play where people act out opinions through posture and movement and/or verbally

- using 'markers' to assess progress, eg activities such as visions and dreams and comparing progress to the vision – How much of the vision has been realised? How far have we moved towards the dream?

- drawing or painting

- 'talking walls' where people pin up their opinions and feelings in words or pictures

The use of alternative and augmentative communication, such as signs and symbol systems, and assistive devices such as speech writers and computers adapted for voice recognition or with different types of switches, will facilitate the participation by people who don't communicate in words or whose verbal communication is limited. Advocates may also be involved for people who find it difficult to represent themselves. There may need to be training in some participatory evaluation techniques for some people, but many of them can be easily learned through just using them.

In summary, the principles for evaluating action research are:

- Evaluation should be built into the research project from the outset and the process agreed by all participants.

- It must have a clear purpose which is understood and agreed by everyone involved.

- Evaluation should include both process and outcomes.

- The evaluation process must be ethical, eg be non-exploitative and have a sound value base built on equality, respect, dignity and individuality.

- It must involve fully the people it represents and take full account of their perspectives.

- The evaluation process must have relevance for, and be accessible to, all participants.

- The resulting information must be presented in ways that make it accessible to everyone.

- Evaluation must be directed towards positive change – something must happen as a result of the evaluation.

ACTIVITY 22: **Evaluating your action research**

This activity is a continuation of the previous one. With reference to the action research described in Activity 21 describe:

● how you will monitor your action research

● how you will evaluate your action research

Comment

It's not enough to do the research, of course, you also need to do something with the information you have gathered. Whatever the purpose for your research the end result needs to be positive change. This means integrating research into practice, something I now discuss. This could be your own research or that of other people.

Assessing the relevance of research and implementing it in your workplace

We're forever hearing about the gap between research and practice, rhetoric and reality. The problem becomes less acute with your own action research because it will have stemmed from workplace practice. However, you also have to consider the relevance and implementation of other people's research and this may be either action research or more traditional research. So what lessons have we learned about translating research into practice?

It's easier to implement your own research in the workplace when the research is participatory

Participatory research is easier to implement because you're not doing it alone, there is shared ownership, there are shared concerns and shared goals. Different perspectives mean that you're more likely to have considered all angles and potential pitfalls. The focus in action research is on real problems and real issues here and now, so it relates to people's concerns and needs.

Implementation also needs to be participatory

This should be a joint venture, with all principle stakeholders involved. There may also be others who should participate. You need to determine who will be affected by the change and how.

You need to anticipate potential problems

Thorough analysis from the outset will enable you to plan possible solutions to problems even before they arise. It may also help to redefine problems and alter the shape of the research.

You are more likely to succeed in implementing research in your workplace if you are systematic and have a clear plan for doing so

Translating research into practice takes time and should be done in well-planned stages, with monitoring procedures built in. You need to plan who will do what and by when.

Incremental change is valid

Small changes which take place gradually over time can make real differences to people's lives. While *transformational* change may be our ultimate goal (equality and social inclusion for people with learning disabilities) *incremental* change is also important to individuals.

Research should lead to changes in knowledge and understanding

The learning which results from your research gives you new insights, adds to your own, and other people's, knowledge and transforms your thinking. New levels of understanding ('deep', as opposed to 'surface' learning) will have a profound effect on your practice and lead to further insights. You are, in effect, developing your own theory. Theory and practice complement and promote one another. This is at the heart of your personal and professional development.

In order to implement someone else's research in the workplace you need to:

- analyse the research and assess its value to your own practice and to your service

- get commitment from other people who will be affected by it

- identify potential problems and barriers and work out ways of dealing with them

- assess the implications for other aspects of your job role

- identify potential allies

- identify possible 'levers' for change in the organisation, eg financial support for change or plans for developing the service

- assess the level of support required and available

- identify the resources required

- have a well-thought-out plan with a realistic timescale and clear measures for assessing progress

Some of these points also apply to the integration of your own research into practice.

One manager told me how she keeps up to date with research:

'Basically I look at what the local authority strategies are with regard to learning disability, but also look at what research says from journals. I look at what the Scottish Consortium [for Learning Disability] comes up with as well. Not just what is happening here but what is happening in other countries too – looking at the different programmes that are used around the world – the internet and all these things.'

She had this advice for other managers:

'I think you have to manage your time very well, because it's such a busy, busy life – and there are so many things – it's easy to get caught up in the bureaucracy. And I think it is always important to stand back and reflect, take time to make sure you are keeping up to date with current trends and things like that – never become complacent. It is about time management and being enthusiastic, making sure you're keeping yourself up to date, always questioning what you're doing, maybe networking with people but also getting support, eg when a problem arises. For example, at that meeting yesterday I knew there were some managers from a different area, but I chatted after the meeting about a problem, gave them the gist of it, asked what they would do in that situation to see what information they might be able to give me. It was a bit like Action Learning, and that can be a very helpful way of learning, but it is about networking and not working in isolation. It was very helpful. There was one thing that I hadn't thought about – not a huge part, but something I hadn't thought about that might help.'

You might like to...

...visit and/or join an academic library near you

...take out a new subscription to a journal or suggest that your organisation does this

...join an online library (see resources section)

...join a special interest group

ACTIVITY 23: **Applying research in practice**

Identify a research article (online or from a journal) that interests you and has relevance for your practice.

Explain why this article interests you.

Describe its relevance for your practice and how you could integrate it into your practice (don't forget involvement of service users).

Describe any problems you anticipate in integrating this article into your practice and how you might overcome them.

Describe how you expect your practice to improve as a result of the application of the research.

Comment

Did you list any of the following problems?

- resistance from colleagues
- lack of support from line manager
- conflicts of interest
- time and workload

Some of these might mean looking at ways of reorganising your work, delegating more and making more time for yourself. Perhaps you need better support from your line manager or other colleagues?

With reference to improving practice, I thought of things like:

- improving relationships with colleagues and service users

- better involvement for service users

- better insights into my own practice, especially from getting to understand other people's perspectives

- new ways of doing things – getting out of a rut

- adding to my own knowledge in a particular work area

- getting me to be more analytical

- making me find other articles about the same topic or related topics

Implementing legislation in the workplace

The pace of change is ever increasing, which can make it difficult to keep up to date with legislation and policy, however essential this is. As a manager or senior practitioner you will have a prime role in keeping up to date with legislation and policy changes, informing others and implementing the changes. To do this you need to:

- have a system for keeping yourself informed about legislative and policy changes – this might be well established in your organisation, or may be in need of improvement

- be able to identify relevant legislation, analyse its implications for your organisation and explain this to colleagues and service users

- be aware of the consequences for yourself and others in the organisation if essential legislation is not adhered to

- have mechanisms for disseminating information relating to legislation and for assessing progress in its implementation

- ensure that relevant legislation is accessible to service users – some documents are now being produced in 'user friendly' formats for people with learning disabilities but there are still many that you will have to adapt

The final activity is about legislation and its relevance to your workplace.

ACTIVITY 24: **Legalisation and the workplace**

Think back over the last two years. List the pieces of legislation that you have had to familiarise yourself with during this period.

Choose one piece and explain why it has relevance for your service.

How successful have you been in implementing this legislation in your workplace?

☐ Totally   ☐ Fairly   ☐ Not very

List any problems you have faced in doing this.

Describe the way your practice has changed to incorporate the requirement of this legislation.

Comment

How did you get on? This activity, like several others in the book, relates directly to your LDAF assignment for the unit on which the book is based. When it comes to legislation we don't have much choice about whether to apply it or not. We can look at legislation as empowering or restricting practice. Legislation is there to protect citizens, to uphold rights and to provide better services. To what extent does it do this in your organisation?

Concluding comments

You've covered a lot of ground since the beginning of this book. Being a manager or a senior practitioner in an organisation which supports people with learning disabilities is a fulfilling job. Otherwise, why would anyone do it? It's also demanding of you as a person and as a professional. Sometimes things move so quickly that you scarcely have time to think about yourself and your own development; you're so busy thinking about other people. It's important to remind yourself that you have a responsibility to yourself, personally and professionally, and that an organisation is only as good as the people who staff it. You are probably already a reflective practitioner. The challenge is to sustain reflection and to develop your own capacity. You owe it to yourself, as well as others. Don't lose sight of your own needs.

After the Reference section there is a Resources section which gives contact details for organisations you might find helpful, as well as a list of useful publications and websites.

References

Adleman, C. (1993) 'Kurt Lewin and the Origins of Action Research' *Educational Action Research* 1, 1, 7–24

Altrichter, H., Posch, P. and Somekh, S. (1993) *Teachers Investigate their Work: An Introduction to the Methods of Action Research* London: Routledge

Argyris, C. and Schon, D. (1978) *Reasoning, Learning and Action: Individual and Organisational* San Francisco: Jossey Bass

Atherton, J.S. (2003) *Learning and Teaching: Learning from Experience* available online at http://www.learningandteaching.info/learning/about.htm

Boud, D., Keogh, R. and Walker, D. (1985) *Reflection: Turning Experience into Learning* London: Kogan Page

Boud, D. and Walker, D. (1998) 'Promoting reflection in professional courses: the challenge of context' *Studies in Higher Education*, 23, 2, 191–206

Clegg, S. (2000) 'Knowing through Reflective Practice in Higher Education' *Educational Action Research* 8, 3, 451–469

Clegg, S., Tan, J. and Saeiddi, S. (2002) 'Reflecting or Acting? Reflective Practice and Continuing Professional Development in Higher Education' *Reflective Practice* 3, 1, 131–146

Clouder, L. and Sellars, J. (2004) 'Reflective practice and clinical supervision: an interprofessional perspective' *Journal of Advanced Nursing* 46, 3, 262-269

Coghlan, D. and Brannick, T. (2001) *Doing action research in your own organization* London: Sage

Cook, T. (2004) 'Reflecting and Learning Together: action research as a vital element of developing understanding and practice' *Educational Action Research* 12, 1, 77–95

Dewey, J. (1933) *How We Think* New York: D.C. Heath

Dick, B. (1997) *Choosing action research* available online at http://www.scu.edu.au/schools/gcm/ar/arp/choice.html

Dick, B. (1999) *What is action research?* available online at http://www.scu.edu.au/schools/gcm/ar/whatisar.html

Dick, B. and Swepson, P. (1997) *Action Research FAQ: 'frequently asked questions' file* available online at http://www.scu.edu.au/schools/gcm/ar/arp/arfaq

Driscoll, J. and Teh, B. (2001) 'The potential of reflective practice to develop individual orthopaedic nurse practitioners and their practice' *Journal of Orthopaedic Nursing* 5, 95–103

Gardner, F. (2001) 'Social Work Students and Self-awareness: how does it happen?' *Reflective Practice* 2, 1, 27–40

Gray, P. *Tackling the effects of stress* details on http:// www.mentalhealth.org.uk/page.cfm?pagecode=PBBFMW

Gustafsson, C. and Fagerberg, I. (2004) 'Reflection, the way to professional development?' *Journal of Clinical Nursing* 13, 271–280

Habermas, J. (1974) *Knowledge and Human Interest* London: Heinemann

Honey, P. and Mumford, A. (1982) *The Manual of Learning Styles* Maidenhead: Peter Honey

Hunt, C. (2001) 'Shifting Shadows: metaphors and maps for facilitating reflective practice' *Reflective Practice* 2, 3, 275–287

Jarvis, P. (1987) *Adult Learning in the Social Context* London: Croom Helm

Kemmis, S. and McTaggart, R. (eds) (1988) *The Action Research Planner* Melbourne: Deakin University

Knowles, M. (1990) *The Adult Learner: A neglected species* 4th edn Houston: Gulf Publishing

Kolb, D. A. (1976) *The Learning Style Inventory: Technical Manual* Boston: McBer

Kolb, D. A. and Fry, R. (1975) 'Toward an applied theory of experiential learning' in C. Cooper (ed) *Theories of Group Process* London: John Wiley

Leitch, R. and Day, C. (2000) 'Action Research and Reflective Practice: towards a holistic view' *Educational Action Research*, 8, 1, 179–193

Maich, N.M., Brown, B. and Royle, J. (2000) '"Becoming" through Reflection and Professional Portfolios: the voice of growth in nurses' *Reflective Practice* 1, 3, 309–324

McGill, I. and Beaty, L. (2001) *Action Learning: a guide for professional, management & educational development* 2nd edn London: Kogan Page

McMahon, T. (1999) 'Is Reflective Practice Synonymous with Action Research?' *Educational Action Research* 7, 1, 163–169

McNamara, C. (1999) *Strong Value of Self-Directed Learning in the Workplace: How Supervisors and Learners Gain Leaps in Learning* available online at http://www.mapnp.org/library/trng_dev/methods/slf_drct.htm

Padak, N. and Padak, G. (undated) *Research to Practice: Guidelines for Planning Action Research Projects* available online at http://literacy.kent.edu/Oasis/Pubs/0200-08.htm

Pask, G. (1988) 'Learning strategies, teaching strategies, and conceptual or learning styles.' in Schmeck R.R. (ed) (1988) *Learning Strategies and Learning Styles* New York: Plenum Press

Rothwell, A. and Ghelipter, S. (2003) 'The Developing Manager: Reflective Learning in Undergraduate Education' *Reflective Practice* 4, 2, 241–254

Saljo, R. (1979) *Learning in the learner's perspective: I. Some commonsense conceptions* Reports from the Institute of Education: University of Gothenburg, 76.

Saunders, B. *The Inside Track Stress* (The Guardian, 10 January 2005)

Schon, D. (1983) *The Reflective Practitioner* New York: Basic Books

Schon, D. (1987) *Educating the Reflective Practitioner* San Francisco: Jossey Bass

Scottish Executive *Towards a New Way of Working* (April 1998) and *Learning Together* (December 1999)

Senge, P. (1990) *The Fifth Discipline: the art and practice of the learning organisation* London: Century Business

Silva, A. (2001) *LOs and Metanoia – Reflective Practice* LO26971 available online at www.learning-org.com

Smith, M. K. (2001) 'David A. Kolb on experiential learning' *the encyclopaedia of informal education* http://www.infed.org

Smith (2003) (Reproduced from the encyclopaedia of informal education www.infed.org

Smith, M. K. (2005) 'Action research' *the encyclopaedia of informal education* www.infed.org/research/b-actres.htm

Stringer, E. T. (1999) *Action Research: A handbook for practitioners* 2nd edn Newbury Park: Sage

Tamkin, P., Barber, L. and Hirsh, W. (1995) IES *Personal Development Plans: Case Studies of Practice* IES Report 280 Brighton: Institute for Employment Studies www.employment-studies.co.uk/pubs/report/php?id=280

Tennant, M. (1997) *Psychology and Adult Learning* 2nd edn London: Routledge

Tilakaratna, S. (1990) *A short note on participatory research* Paper presented to seminar of Sri Lankan social scientists and community specialists in January 1990 available online at http://www.caledonia.org.uk/research.htm

Todhunter, C. (2001) 'Undertaking Action Research: Negotiating the Road Ahead' *Social Research Update, Issue 34* available online at http://www.soc.surrey.ac.uk/sru/SRU34.html

Trumper, L. (2004) Personal development plans available online at www.businesshotlinepublications.co.uk

Walker, M. (1993) 'Developing the Theory and Practice of Action Research: a South African Case' *Educational Action Research* 1, 1, 95–109

Ward, L. and Watson, D. (undated) *Doing Research – And Doing It Right, A Community Fund Guide to Ethical Aspects of Research Grants Applications* available online www.c-f.org. uk/about-us/our-publications/research-grants/ research-guide.pdf

Watson, J.S. and Wilcox, S. (2000) 'Reading for Understanding: Methods of Reflecting on Practice' *Reflective Practice* 1, 1, 57–67

Webb, M. W. (2003) *A Definitive Critique of Experiential Learning Theory* available online at http://cc.ysu.edu/~mnwebb

Yoong, P. (1999) 'Making sense of group support systems facilitation: a reflective practice perspective' *Information Technology and People* 12, 1, 86–112

Resources

Books and articles

Angwin, J. (1998) *The essence of action research* Geelong: Deakin Centre for Education and Change, Deakin University

Argyris, C. (1999) *On organizational learning* 2nd edn Oxford: Blackwell.

Bannister, F. and Reymeni, D. (1999) *Value Perception in IT Investment Decisions* Electronic Journal of Information Systems Evaluation, Vol. 2, www.ejise.com/volume-2/volume2-issue2/issue2-art1.htm

Barbour, R. S., and Kitzinger, J. (eds) (1999) *Developing focus group research: politics, theory and practice* London: Sage

Batehup, L. (ed) (1999) *Facilitating change in nursing practice: studies in action research* New York: Churchill Livingstone

Bolton, G. (2000) *Reflective Practice Writing and Professional Development* London: Paul Chapman

Bray, J. N., Lee, J., Smith, L. L. and Yorks, L. (eds) (2000) *Collaborative inquiry in practice: action, reflection, and making meaning* Thousand Oaks, Ca: Sage

Chappell, A. L (2000) 'Emergence of participatory methodology in learning disability research: understanding the context' *British Journal of Learning Disabilities* 28, 1, 38–43

Clarke, A. (2001) *Learning Organisations: What are they and how to become one* Leicester: National Organisation for Adult Learning

Coghlan, D. and Brannick, T. (2001) *Doing research in your own organization* London: Sage

Cottrell, S. (2003) *Skills for Success: The Personal Development Planning Handbook* Basingstoke: Palgrave Macmillan

Dadds, M. and Hart, S. (eds) (2001) *Doing practitioner research differently* London: Falmer

De Koning, K. and Martin, M. (eds) (1996) *Participatory research and health: issues and experiences* London: Zed Books

Denscombe, M. (1998) *The good research guide for small-scale social research projects* Buckingham: Open University Press

Denzin, N. K. and Lincoln, Y. S. (eds) (2000) *Handbook of qualitative research* 2nd edn Thousand Oaks, Ca: Sage

Elliott, H. (1997) *The Use of Diaries in Sociological Research on Health Experience* www.socresonline.org.uk/2/2/7.html

Fuller, R. and Petch, A. (1995) *Practitioner research: the reflexive social worker* Buckingham: Open University Press

Ghaye, T., Gillespie, D. and Lillyman, S. (eds) (2000) *Empowerment Through Reflection: the narratives of health care* London: Quay Books, Mark Allen Publishers

Glesne, C. (1999) *Becoming qualitative researchers: an introduction* 2nd edn New York: Longman

Goodley, D. (2004) 'Editorial: The place of people with "learning difficulties" in disability studies and research: introduction to this special issue' *British Journal of Learning Disabilities* 32, 2, 49–52

Gould, N. (2000) 'Becoming a learning organisation: A social work example' *Social Work Education* 19, 6, 585–596.

Grbich, C. (1999) *Qualitative research in health: an introduction* London: Sage

Greenwood, D. J. and Levin, M. (1998) *Introduction to action research: social research for social change* Thousand Oaks, Ca: Sage

Harrison, L., Johnson, K., Hillier, L. and Strong, R. (2002) '"Nothing about us without us": the ideals of participatory action research with people with an intellectual disability' *Scandinavian Journal of Disability* 5, 2, 75–81

Hart, E. and Bond, M. (1995) *Action Research for Health and Social Care: A Guide to Practice* Buckingham: Open University Press

Kiernan, C. (1999) 'Participation in research by people with learning disability: origins and issues' *British Journal of Learning Disabilities* 27, 2, 43–47

Learning organisations: A self-assessment resource pack available online at http://www.scie.org.uk/publications/learningorgs/index.asp

McNiff, J., Lomax, P. and Whitehead, J. (2003) *You and Your Action Research Project* London: RoutledgeFalmer

McNiff, J. and Whitehead, J. (2000) *Action research in organisations* London: Routledge

Moon, J. (2000) *Reflection in Learning and Professional Development: Theory and Practice* London: RoutledgeFalmer

Moon, J. (2004) *A Handbook of Reflective and Experiential Learning: Theory and Practice* London: RoutledgeFalmer

Morton-Cooper, A. (2000) *Action research in health care* Oxford: Blackwell Science

Mullen, E. (1995) 'Pursuing knowledge through qualitative research' *Social Work Research*, 19, 1, 29–32

Newton, C. and Marsh, P. (1993) *Training in partnership* York: Joseph Rowntree Foundation

Pedler, M. and Aspinwall, K. (1998) *A concise guide to the learning organisation* London: Lemos and Crane

Redmond, B. (2004) *Reflection in Action: Developing Reflective Practice in Health and Social Services* Aldershot: Ashgate

Rolfe, G., Freshwater, D. and Jasper, M. (2001) *Critical Reflection for Nursing and the Helping Professions: A User's Guide* Basingstoke: Palgrave Macmillan

Rosen, G. (ed) (1999) *Managing team development* London: National Institute for Social Work

Stringer, E. T. (1999) *Action Research: A Handbook for Practitioners* Thousand Oaks, Ca: Sage

Walmsley, J. (2001) 'Normalisation, emancipatory research and learning disability' *Disability and Society* 16, 2, 187–205

Walmsley, J. (2004) 'Inclusive learning disability research: the (nondisabled) researcher's role' *British Journal of Learning Disabilities* 32, 2, 65–75

Williams, V. (1999) 'Researching together' *British Journal of Learning Disabilities* 27, 2, 48–51

Williams, V. and Simons, K. (2005) 'More researching together: the role of nondisabled researchers in working with People First members' *British Journal of Learning Disabilities* 33, 1, 6–14

Journals

British Journal of Learning Disabilities
Blackwell Quarterly
http://www.blackwellpublishing.com/journal.asp?ref=1354-4187&site=1

Community Care Reed Business Information
Weekly
http://www.communitycare.co.uk/Home/default.asp

Disability and Society
Routledge 7 issues per annum
http://www.tandf.co.uk/journals/titles/09687599.asp

Educational Action Research
Triangle Quarterly
http://www.triangle.co.uk/ear

Health and Social Care in the Community
Blackwell 6 issues per annum
http://www.blackwellpublishing.com/journal.asp?ref=0966-0410&site=1

Journal of Applied Research in Intellectual Disabilities
Blackwell Quarterly
http://www.blackwellpublishing.com/journal.
asp?ref=1360-2322&site=1

Learning Disabilities Research and Practice
Blackwell Quarterly
http://www.blackwellpublishing.com/journal.
asp?ref=0938-8982&site=1

Learning Disability Bulletin
British Institute of Learning Disabilities
Quarterly
http://www.bild.org.uk/publications/journals

Learning in Health and Social Care
Blackwell Quarterly
http://www.blackwellpublishing.com/journal.
asp?ref=1473-6853&site=1

Reflective Practice
Routledge Quarterly
http://www.tandf.co.uk/journals/
titles/14623943.asp

Social Sciences
The regular newsletter of the ESRC
3 issues per annum
http://www.esrcsocietytoday.
ac.uk/ESRCInfoCentre/about/CI/CP/
Social%5FSciences

Websites

Website addresses were correct at time of going to press.

http://www.scie-socialcareonline.org.uk

Social Care Online provides free access to a range of information and research on all aspects of social care, drawn from a range of resources including journal articles, websites, research reviews, legislation and government documents, and service user knowledge.

http://www.scie.org.uk

Social Care Institute for Excellence

http://www.nelh.nhs.uk

National Electronic Library for Health

http://www.infed.org/research/
b-actres.htm

An open, independent, not-for-profit site established to provide opportunities for people to explore the theory and practice of informal education and lifelong learning,

http://www.kingsfund.org.uk

The King's Fund, an independent charitable foundation with a mission to improve health and health care through research, analysis and debate, and capacity building and offer essential resources to people working in health and social care.

http://www.jrf.org.uk/about

The Joseph Rowntree Foundation, one of the largest social policy research and development charities in the UK.

http://www.esrc.ac.uk/esrccontent/
connect/indexpub.asp

The Economic and Social Research Council (ESRC), the UK's leading research funding and training agency addressing economic and social concerns.

http://www.nuffieldtrust.org.uk

The Nuffield Trust promotes independent analysis and informed debate on UK health care policy with the aim of improving health and health care.

http://www.york.ac.uk/inst/iriss

The Institute for Research in the Social Sciences (IRISS) is one of the largest multi-disciplinary centres for social science research in the UK.

http://www.rdforum.nhs.uk

The NHS R&D Forum, a network for those involved in planning and managing research in health and social care.